A IDAN'S FAT E

She could hear the TV news . . .

'. . . The accident occurred just minutes ago. The teenage driver was killed instantly when his green Cobra exploded in a gigantic fireball – '

Aidan!

TITLES IN THE POWER SERIES
by JESSE HARRIS

THE POWER

AIDAN'S FATE

by Jesse Harris

RED FOX

A Red Fox Book

Published by Random House Children's Books
20 Vauxhall Bridge Road, London SW1V 2SA

A division of Random House UK Ltd

London Melbourne Sydney Auckland Johannesburg
and agencies throughout the world

First published in the United States by
Alfred A. Knopf, Inc. 1992

Red Fox edition 1993

Copyright © Parachute Press, Inc. 1992

The right of Jesse Harris to be identified as the
author of this work has been asserted by her in
accordance with the Copyright, Designs and
Patents Act, 1988

Phototypeset by Intype, London
Printed and bound in Great Britain by
Cox & Wyman Ltd, Reading, Berkshire

ISBN 0 09 922131 4

PROLOGUE

It's a dark, frozen night in the dead of winter. The street is deserted. Suddenly a car speeds by.

A handsome, teenage boy sits behind the wheel. He drives fast. As the car rushes past the streetlights they light up the inside of his car with a series of flashes. On, off, on, off, the flashes of light shine on the wheel. The teenager grips the wheel with one white-knuckled hand. The cuff of his shirt is bright red. On, off, on, off.

Snow begins to fall, lightly at first, then heavier and heavier. The boy flicks on the windshield wipers. They move at high speed, but the windshield jams up with snow anyway.

Tick tick tick tick. . . . What's that sound? Is it the wipers?

No. It's something else. What?

1

The boy keeps his eyes on the road. His face is drawn, tense. He looks worried.

Tick tick tick tick . . .

Why doesn't he hear that sound? What is it?

He takes his eyes off the road and glances down to his right. There is a Band-Aid on his left cheek. What is he looking at? Is there someone else in the car?

He makes a sharp turn. The car skids. He wrenches the wheel and pulls out of the spin. He's driving so fast. Too fast! He glances nervously in his rearview mirror.

The ticking grows louder.

And louder. And louder . . .

He still doesn't hear it. Why?

TICK TICK TICK TICK TICK –

Where is the sound coming from?

The trunk of the car! There it is. There it is! It's a bomb!

The ticking stops.

It stops for only the briefest of seconds . . .

The boy turns around. His face fills with horror. What does he see?

And then . . . the car explodes.

CHAPTER 1

February 2, 8:00 a.m.
. . . tick tick tick tick . . .

The alarm clock on McKenzie Gold's night-stand rang piercingly. She sat bolt upright and fumbled for the clock, slapping it off.

Her heart pounded and she was drenched in sweat.

It was a dream. Just a dream. She repeated the words to herself over and over again, trying to calm her racing heart.

Staring up at the ceiling, she struggled to focus her sleepy eyes. Above her the familiar crack curved along the ceiling like a dragon's tail. She *was* in her own bed. In her own room. In her parents' house. In Lakeville. It's Saturday morning, she told herself. February second.

Her boyfriend, Aidan, was home. Probably

still asleep. His car hadn't exploded. He was alive and well.

Then she heard it again. *Tick tick tick . . .* Her head jerked toward the sound.

Her green windup alarm clock sat on the bedside table, grinning at her. The clock was last month's birthday present from her eight-year-old brother, Jimmy. The clock's face was a real face – a smiling man in the moon with tiny, black eyes. The moon face looked as if it knew something. *Tick tick tick . . .*

That must be what had caused her nightmare, she decided. It was just the ticking of the clock, and her anxiety about the alarm going off.

Still, she had good reason to be worried . . .

McKenzie had been having vivid dreams since she was little. In itself, that wasn't so unusual. Everyone dreamed. But unlike those of most kids, her dreams – and sometimes her nightmares – had a strange habit of coming true.

McKenzie knew she had special powers. She'd known it since she was a kid. Lately, though, those powers seemed to be growing stronger and stronger. She not only dreamed, she could sense things: she could tell what others were thinking and feel acutely the good and bad energies around her.

She rubbed her face, trying to come fully awake. Then, tucking her straight auburn hair behind her ears, she touched the crystal pendant at her neck. It was a gift from her grandmother, and because she somehow felt safer whenever she wore it, she always did. She fingered the jewel softly. Then she remembered Aidan's car exploding in her dream and shuddered.

She slipped off her long red T-shirt, tossed it on the bed, and opened her closet door. She shivered a little with the cold.

Two yellow eyes stared back at her from the top shelf.

'Aw, Blue,' she said with a sigh. 'Did you get shut in here again?'

Her black cat may have been old, but he hadn't lost any of his curiosity. He sneaked into her closet every chance he got. 'Why didn't you wake me up?' she asked him. Blue opened his mouth and let out a mournful half meow.

She picked up the cat and dropped him gently on the bed. 'You're a silly old thing,' she said as she rubbed Blue where he liked it most, right behind the ears.

She was feeling better. There was nothing like getting out of bed to make a nightmare go away. She loved her family's old Victorian house. She always felt safe and loved here, that it was a place where nothing bad could ever happen. Her powers were accepted, even applauded, by her parents and brother. Home was a good place to be.

There was a knock at her door. 'Just a sec,' she called. She went back to the closet, yanked out a black turtleneck, and hastily pulled it on.

'I'm going to the market, lazybones,' her mother said through the door. 'You want anything?'

McKenzie opened the door and grinned sleepily. 'Hi.'

Her mom was wearing a forest-green blouse that beautifully set off her very short auburn hair. Like her daughter, Joanne Gold was tall, slim, and pretty.

'Hi, sweetie.' Her mom smiled warmly. 'I hate to tell you this, but you lost the Gold wake-up contest. You're the last one out of bed.'

McKenzie yawned and idly ruffled her hair. 'What's my punishment?'

'Your punishment is you can have anything you want from my upcoming shopping spree. I got a call this morning – the Donaldsons accepted the Felders' offer.'

This was great news. Mrs. Gold was a realtor, and the Donaldson house would bring her a big commission.

6

'Okay,' McKenzie told her. 'I'll take a Porsche.'

'One Porsche.' Her mom wrote it down on her shopping list. She turned to go, then turned back. 'Keep an eye on your father while I'm gone, would you? He's *creating*.'

McKenzie laughed and promised she would. After her mom left, she went down to the kitchen and poured a bowl of Cheerios. She heard the familiar sound of grinding metal coming from the backyard and glanced out the window.

Outside, her father, Shelby Gold, was working on an aluminum sculpture. He was trying to attach the left leg to an eight-foot-tall elephant. It was supposed to be a political sculpture, with the elephant symbolizing the Republican party – much to McKenzie's dismay, her father was a staunch Republican. She looked away. Dad! How was she supposed to have friends over with *that* in the backyard?

Her father ran the local hardware store. But McKenzie knew he was happiest at home, where he could be with his family and work on his projects.

Inspired by an old horror movie on TV, her father, Jimmy, and she had spent one October trying to rig a metal dragon that breathed real fire for Halloween. It never worked. The dragon kept tipping and falling. But they'd had a good time anyway, especially when they gave up and used the lighter fluid to start the outdoor grill. Then they toasted marshmallows. Neighbor kids got wind of the marshmallow toasting and flooded to the yard for the warm treats. Mr. Gold donned the metal dragon head and danced around the barbecue's fire. It was the kind of thing McKenzie loved him for.

The morning paper lay on the kitchen table. She glanced at the day's headlines. Preparations were already beginning for Lakeville's Annual Winter Carnival and Fireworks Festival, which would be held at the end of the month. She was psyched – the winter carnival was an event not to miss!

She carried her cereal bowl into the den, where Jimmy was watching TV. On the screen two Saturday superheroes fought to the death. Her brother wasn't watching, though. He and his friend Nick were playing with toy metal racing cars.

'Watch out!' he snapped at his older sister. 'You're right in the middle of the highway.'

'*Pardonnez-moi*,' said McKenzie, stepping to the side.

'GO!' yelled Nick. The two boys zoomed their cars toward each other along the rug.

'BOOM!' yelled Jimmy as the cars crashed.

McKenzie paused in mid-swallow. Jimmy and Nick both raised their cars into the air in a slow-motion accident. Suddenly she was picturing her dream. She saw Aidan at the wheel, driving so fast, that tense look on his face, the pelting snow.

She tried to shake off the image, but it wouldn't go away. It kept playing out, like the slow-motion accident Jimmy and Nick had just staged. It didn't stop until she had recalled it all – until she had remembered seeing Aidan's car blow up, once again, in a shimmering ball of hot, white flame.

'Oh, yeah,' Aidan told the group, 'before I forget, there's a photo contest I want to tell you guys about.'

He sorted through the pile of photos on his desk, looking for the article he had clipped from that morning's *Lakeville Times*.

This was Aidan's third week running the photo club at the Lakeville Community Center. It wasn't as if he didn't have enough to do already. He was studying karate; taking photos for the *Guardian*, the school paper; working part-time at the Gap; playing keyboard in his friend Boz's band; and tutoring math. But when Mr. Grunwald at the center had asked him, he just couldn't resist. The club met twice a week, on Wednesdays and Saturdays. He liked all of the five kids who had signed up.

'Here we go.' He waved the newspaper article. 'I'll put this on the bulletin board so you can all read it. It says they're going to award twenty-five dollars each to the best photos of the winter carnival.'

'Do they have age groups or anything?' asked the twelve-year-old in the front row.

Aidan quickly scanned the article. 'Yeah. Twelve and under.' He looked around at his young club members. 'That's all of you, right? Plus thirteen to eighteen. That's me. And nineteen and up.'

'What if one of us wins and you don't?' asked another kid.

Aidan smiled. 'That'll just prove what an awesome teacher I am.'

He glanced at Kevin Larsen, the skinny ten-year-old who always sat in the back row, his hands folded tightly on his desk. The boy's expression was serious, attentive.

Aidan tried hard not to make the club meetings like a classroom. He had suffered through too many strict teachers himself. But Kevin seemed to have some self-discipline. Aidan smiled at Kevin; the boy smiled back, revealing a mouthful of slightly crooked teeth that needed braces. There was something about the kid that got to Aidan. He seemed older than his ten years.

If anyone wins, I hope it's Kevin, Aidan thought. Somehow he looks like he could use a break.

'Anyway, the article is right here,' Aidan told the group, 'so you'll all remember.' He pushpinned the clipping to the bulletin board. 'The festival's not till the end of this month. You have plenty of time to practice your photography before then.'

He ran a hand through his already tousled sandy hair. 'Any questions?'

'How could I photograph my toy submarine and make it look like it's really real?' asked a seven-year-old.

'Uh, good question,' Aidan said. 'But you know what? I'm going to have to answer that at our next meeting, because' – he glanced at the clock – 'time's up.'

The group laughed. 'You're just trying to get out of it,' the little boy teased.

Aidan smiled. 'Maybe I am,' he admitted. 'But that's really all we have time for today. Remember to leave your practice rolls in the bin so I can develop them, and I'll see you on Wednesday.'

Ten minutes later he had finished straightening up. He locked up the darkroom, flicked the lights, and, tossing on his blue down vest, headed for the front door.

Outside, on the icy steps of the center, sat Kevin. He looked up as Aidan came out. He had tied the hood of his sweatshirt very tightly. His hands were stuffed into the front pocket. His lips looked blue.

'Kevin!' said Aidan. 'What's the matter? You need a lift?'

The boy shook his head.

Aidan frowned. 'C'mon. Let me take you home.'

'I gotta wait,' the boy mumbled.

The sound of a car with a noisy transmission turned both their heads to the street. A small, seedy-looking yellow Lion swerved to a stop across from the center. Kevin got to his feet.

'Thanks anyway for the offer! See ya!' he yelled as he ran.

Who's *that*? Aidan wondered as Kevin hopped into the passenger seat. Whoever it was, Aidan hoped Kevin would be okay riding with him. The car didn't exactly look safe.

Aidan shook his head. Somehow the dilapidated state of the car didn't surprise him. The boy had an air of sadness about him, as if he had already experienced plenty of bad things. The yellow car peeled out with a spray of gravel.

That night it began to sleet and the temperature dropped ten degrees. The roads turned to solid ice. Still, Aidan insisted that he and McKenzie go ahead with their planned date, dancing at a local eighteen-and-under disco, The China Club. They went with McKenzie's best friend, Lilith Caine – nicknamed Lilicat – and her blind date, Kirk Davies.

Kirk was a cousin of a friend of Aidan's friend Boz. Neither McKenzie nor Aidan had met him before. 'What do you think of him?' Aidan yelled in McKenzie's ear, trying to be heard over the music's booming beat.

McKenzie looked across the dance floor. Kirk was dancing close to Lilicat, looking down into her eyes. He was very good looking, with long blond hair, sharp features, and a strong jaw. 'He's okay!' she yelled back.

'What?' Aidan shouted.

She repeated it twice, then gave up. Putting her arms around his neck, McKenzie moved Aidan out onto the dance floor.

'Lilicat seems to like him,' Aidan said into her ear as they danced.

McKenzie looked over at Lilicat. Her friend was shimmying, doing moves she and McKenzie had practiced in the mirror last week. Aidan was right. Lilicat did like him.

The club's deejay glided from one fast song

13

into the next. Now he was playing the new pop tune 'Love is Fate.'

'It was fate that we met,' sang a woman's silky voice. 'And I can't get . . . you outta my heaaarrt . . .'

'Hi, guys.' It was Kirk. He danced easily alongside Aidan and McKenzie. 'Lilith went to the bathroom,' he explained, answering the question in McKenzie's eyes.

'Here she comes,' she told him, spotting Lilicat across the dance floor.

'Listen,' Kirk said to Aidan. 'How about if I dance this one with McKenzie?'

The frown on Aidan's face gave McKenzie a thrill. They'd been going out for months now. She was glad he still cared enough to be a little jealous.

Aidan quickly recovered. 'Sure, go ahead!' he yelled over the crashing music.

Kirk was a great dancer, McKenzie had to admit. But then he started dancing really close. She danced backward, rocking to the beat. But he followed. Soon his face was only inches away, his intense eyes locked on hers. 'You've got the cutest freckles I've ever seen,' he told her.

She pretended not to have heard and danced harder, her steps carrying her into her own orbit away from Kirk. It was nice to have gotten the compliment. But it made her uncomfortable. Was she wrong, or was that a come-on? She must be wrong. He wouldn't do that, not with Aidan and Lilicat right there.

McKenzie was relieved when the song ended. She quickly rejoined Lilicat and Aidan, who stood off to the side. McKenzie saw that Lilicat had freshened her makeup in the bathroom. She seemed to have fallen hard for Kirk. McKenzie hoped Lilicat wouldn't get hurt – Kirk was a little too slick.

They danced for another hour, but McKenzie made it a point to stay close to Aidan. Finally they all agreed they'd had enough and left the club. They got into Aidan's car and drove toward Kirk's house, their first stop on the way home.

'Is that guy hot or what?' Lilicat said after Kirk had gone inside. She shivered playfully and threw back her long black hair. 'He was, like, the blind date of my dreams.'

'He was pretty cute,' McKenzie agreed, deciding not to say more than that.

'Did you think he was *so* good looking?' Aidan asked McKenzie, after dropping off Lilicat. He had parked in front of the Golds' house. Outside the car, snow sifted down, enveloping them in whiteness.

Even though his hair was always mussed and

he had a slightly crooked nose from a childhood accident, Aidan was very handsome. The fact that Kirk was technically more handsome wasn't something McKenzie was about to tell him. Besides, she liked Aidan's looks better. There was laughter in his eyes, warmth in his smile. He was real – not some model type impressed with his own image.

'He was good looking, but not compared to you,' she told him. He smiled at her, obviously savoring the compliment.

McKenzie stroked his cheek and kissed him. She loved him so much!

Then she thought of her nightmare. Usually she liked to tell Aidan everything. But she didn't want to come off like his mother or something, telling him to be careful because she had had a nightmare.

But what if something did happen to him? What if she never saw him again? Suddenly her eyes misted with tears. 'Hey,' she said softly, kissing him again and again.

For almost twenty minutes they sat holding each other and kissing. Finally she broke away from his embrace and went inside for the night.

She found her dad waiting up in the living room. He sat in his big blue bathrobe, sipping hot cocoa. 'I made it for you,' he told her with a wink, 'but I ended up drinking it myself.'

She laughed and thanked him. 'It's the thought that counts.' After he had gone upstairs, she made another cup, adding plenty of tiny marshmallows. She sat for a long time watching the snow fall outside the kitchen window. It was coming down even harder now. It made her feel peaceful, being inside and warm on such a stormy night.

Then she thought of Aidan, who had to drive home in this weather. His brand-new low-slung green Cobra sports car simply wasn't meant for winter. The roads were icy, and he didn't even have snow tires.

Tick tick tick . . .

She looked around. The kitchen wall clock was electric, and silent. Where was that faint ticking coming from? It seemed to be deep inside her own brain.

Unless . . . She remembered her dream. The ticking bomb! 'No. That's stupid!' she decided, forcing herself to put it out of her head once again.

She carried her mug of cocoa up the stairs. The sound of light snoring wafted out of Jimmy's room. She smiled. This was one of the only times she consistently felt affection for her younger brother: when he was sleeping!

Next she passed her parents' bedroom. There

was a strip of light under the door. She could hear the TV news . . .

'. . . The accident occurred just minutes ago. The teenage driver was killed instantly when his green Cobra exploded in a gigantic fire-ball – '

Aidan!

CHAPTER 2

McKenzie felt as if someone had punched her in the stomach. Barely able to breathe, she clutched at the wall, determined not to faint.

It had happened. Just as she saw it.

No! No!

Her mind wouldn't accept that Aidan was gone. It couldn't be. She wouldn't let it be! Every nerve ending in her body suddenly cried out with rage and denial. She wouldn't believe it – not until she saw it for herself.

McKenzie burst through the bedroom door, racing straight for the TV. She ran right past her father's side of the bed, bumping his elbow; Shelby spilled his cocoa.

'What did they say?' McKenzie demanded. *'What did they say?'*

'McKenzie, calm down!' scolded Joanne from the bed. 'What's the matter with you?'

A picture of a short, red-haired teen with glasses flashed on the screen. 'His name was Andy Mulroney,' intoned the announcer. 'He was nineteen. Now he's dead.'

'Oh, wow,' moaned McKenzie. She sank to the carpet. 'I thought – I'm sorry.'

'You thought what?' Shelby asked.

'Wait!' McKenzie pleaded. 'I've got to listen to this.'

The news anchorman was back on-camera. 'As we reported last week, Target, the maker of Cobra cars, has issued a nationwide recall.'

On the TV a car was being rear-ended in slow motion. It burst into towering flames. 'The rear location of the gas tank in the Cobra,' explained the announcer, 'is believed to be the cause of these explosions.'

'That's Aidan's car,' McKenzie told her parents. 'The exact same make!'

'Oh, my!' Joanne cried. 'That's horrible.'

'Call him right away,' said Shelby, mopping at the spilled cocoa with a tissue.

McKenzie called from her parents' bedside phone.

'Hullo?'

'Aidan! Oh, I'm so glad you got home safe.' She looked at her parents as relief washed over her, and they smiled back.

'What recall?' Aidan asked as she started to tell him.

She repeated the broadcaster's message.

'Whew!' he said. 'Good thing we were the only ones crazy enough to be out driving tonight! If we had gotten rear-ended . . .'

'Don't even think about it,' she said.

'You see.' He laughed. 'This proves what I always say. I'm a lucky guy.'

'Lucky? Your car is a deathtrap on wheels.'

'I'll drive it back to the dealership tomorrow,' he promised.

'Drive it back?' McKenzie nearly screeched. 'You shouldn't get in that car ever again.'

He laughed. 'I guess you're right. I'll call the car dealership first thing in the morning and have it towed.'

Joanne was tapping her watch. 'I'll talk to you tomorrow,' McKenzie told Aidan. 'Promise me again that you won't drive the Cobra.'

'I promise,' he said solemnly.

She hung up and told her parents, 'He's fine.'

In the bathroom she peeled off her clothes, letting them drop in a pile, and turned the shower on hot and full.

Now she could really relax. Though she had tried to put it out of her mind, that nightmare must have been bothering her all day. The car recall obviously explained the strange dream.

21

So it *was* a warning. The trunk of Aidan's car had been a ticking time bomb, just waiting to go off.

She let out a long, slow breath. She still hadn't learned to trust her instincts fully enough. Her dreams always meant *something*, she reminded herself. The confusing part was figuring out exactly what that something was.

Naked, she reached a hand into the shower stall to feel the water temperature. Too hot. She reached in cautiously, trying to turn the faucet without getting scalded.

And as she reached, she looked toward the window.

And saw him.

He was looking in through the bathroom window. His face was close to the glass.

A cruel face.

Crew cut.

Denim jacket.

A skull earring dangling from one ear.

He was staring right at her.

CHAPTER 3

The steam in the bathroom quickly fogged the window. McKenzie's heart was beating like a jackhammer. She wrapped a towel around herself as she rushed to the window. She wiped the steam away with her fist. No one was there.

She jerked the window wide open and stuck her head outside. Freezing air rushed at her bare skin, and it was only then that she realized the truth.

There was no way she could have seen a face at the window. Because there was no place for a Peeping Tom to *stand* outside the second-floor bathroom window. There was no tree there. No porch ledge. He would have had to have been floating in midair!

Shivering violently, she slammed the window and locked it. A cold dread ran through her. The face had been so creepy! So evil! So real!

She shook with a sudden chill. The warm shower looked inviting. All she wanted to do was step into it and forget this day. She stepped into the stall. As soon as she had her head under the water, she heard a horrible laugh. It came from nowhere – above her, below – and it filled the room, echoing against the tiles.

Shaking with fright, she turned off the water and stepped back out of the shower.

There was no one there. There was no one outside the window, no one outside the bathroom door.

But the laugh continued.

A wicked laugh. Mean, raspy, cold.

And she had no idea where it was coming from.

'He is such a great guy,' Lilicat gushed. 'So affectionate.'

'Ooh,' cooed McKenzie, teasing. 'I'll bet.'

She thought again of that moment on the dance floor. Maybe Kirk was a little *too* affectionate – with everyone.

It was Sunday night. McKenzie was talking on the kitchen phone while Jimmy stuffed his face with Mallomars, refusing to give her any privacy. 'Hi, Aidan!' he called into the phone.

'Jimmy says "Hi, Aidan," ' McKenzie told her best friend.

'Tell him I say "Hi, Susan," ' Lilicat joked.

'Lilicat says "Hi, Jerkface. Get out of the kitchen and let me talk." '

'It's not lover boy?' he said with his mouth full. 'I didn't know you ever talked to anyone else.'

'Out!'

Jimmy stayed right where he was and gave her a taunting smile.

'Kirk already asked me out for Tuesday,' said Lilicat.

'Cool. What are you going to do?'

'I don't know. I thought maybe he should just sneak up to my room after my mom goes to bed.'

'Playing hard to get, huh?' McKenzie laughed.

'Jimmy!' Shelby called from the den. 'I'm ready to play Nintendo!'

Jimmy raced out of the room with two cookies in each hand.

'Our little spy is gone,' McKenzie told her friend. 'We can talk.'

'Great,' said Lilicat. 'Listen, do you think this is going to be *the* one for me? Be honest. I mean, do you have the same feeling about this that I do?'

'I don't know,' McKenzie said cautiously.

'Come on! You have to tell me if you think it's going to happen,' Lilicat pressed.

'Lilicat, how do *I* know?'

'Well, you *do* sometimes know things before they happen.'

Besides Aidan, Lilicat was the only friend McKenzie trusted with the secret of her strange visions. She didn't tell Lilicat everything, though. Right now she had no intention of mentioning what her intuition was telling her. She suspected that she, Aidan, Lilicat, and Kirk had been on their first and *last* double date. Why upset Lilicat? Besides, some things a person just had to discover for herself. 'I can't predict everything,' McKenzie hedged.

'Well, I'll tell you *my* prediction,' Lilicat went on. 'I bet he and I are going steady by winter carnival.'

'Mmm,' McKenzie replied vaguely.

'Just tell me this. Don't you think he's sexy?'

'Lilicat,' McKenzie teased, 'I already told you he was sexy about sixteen times.'

'Make it seventeen.'

'He's sexy.'

'And you know what else was cool? It was like we were in tune with each other, right from the start. Like we already knew each other. Like we could read each other's minds or something.'

McKenzie wasn't listening.

A strange feeling had come over her. She suddenly felt that she had better call Aidan. But she had no idea why.

The nightmare was over, she reminded herself. But she couldn't stop the impulse. The more she tried to talk herself out of it, the stronger it grew. She *had* to call.

'Lilicat,' she interrupted. 'Can I call you back?'

'Oh, great,' her friend said. 'Am I that boring?'

'I'll call you right back,' she repeated. She had programmed Aidan's number into the phone's automatic dialing feature. She depressed the automatic dial.

'Hi,' McKenzie said when Aidan answered. 'It's me.'

'Hey! What's up?'

Good question, she thought. She had no idea why she was calling. 'What's all that yelling?' she stalled.

Aidan snorted. 'My brothers and I are having another peaceful discussion.'

'About?'

'Who should drive through the snow to rent a video.'

'You're not driving *your* car, are you?'

'They towed it this morning. Just like I promised. Hey – if we don't rent a war movie or something too stupid, you want to join us?'

McKenzie didn't answer. She couldn't. It was as if something had suddenly begun tapping on her brain.

'Mack? Are you there?'

'Uh-huh,' she mumbled. But she wasn't. Because in her head she once again saw Aidan driving down the deserted street.

'Mack?' Aidan asked.

But she could barely hear him now. Loud music had begun to play in her head. It was coming from the radio in Aidan's car . . .

'It was fate that we met,' the woman's silky voice sings on the radio. 'And I can't get . . . you outta my heaaarrt . . .'

'Mack . . . ?' Aidan's voice was growing more and more distant. As if in a trance, McKenzie gently set the phone down on the counter.

The car swerves. Aidan wrenches the wheel.

'Love songs,' croons the deejay on the car radio. 'On this special day we've got nothing but love songs, all day long.'

Aidan drives so fast. He wears a Band-Aid on his left cheek. The snow falls harder. The streetlights flash through the car. On, off, on, off. He grips the wheel with one hand. His fingers are white. The cuff of his shirt is bright red.

Tick tick tick . . .

That sound. Again. That sound.

She must have been wrong about the bomb. The explosion was due to a faulty fuel tank.

Not a bomb.

Could the ticking be from the clock?

The clock glows green in the car's darkness: 7:56.

But it's silent.

Tick tick tick . . .

No, the ticking must be coming from the trunk.

Suddenly the image of the clock enlarges. It flashes several times in rapid succession. Each time, the minute hand jerks slowly forward – four minutes till eight, three minutes till eight, two minutes till –

And then – No! Oh, no! – the car explodes.

'We must have gotten disconnected,' Aidan mumbled to himself. 'Maybe it's this storm.' The shouting in the TV room was growing intense. Aidan hung up the phone and then called McKenzie back. Busy.

'Yo, Patrick!' Aidan shouted at one of his younger brothers, trying to be heard over the racket. 'I'll tell you what. *I'll* get the flick.' He crossed the hall to the coatrack. 'Unless you guys would rather argue all night. I mean, the store is going to close any minute.' I'll pick up the movie and then stop at McKenzie's house on the way back, Aidan told himself. There was something unsettling about the way the phone connection had broken off.

He glanced at his watch. Eleven minutes till eight.

'Uh-oh. I knew it was only a matter of time. You've finally flipped your lid.'

McKenzie blinked. Jimmy was standing in the kitchen doorway, looking at her intently. 'Are you okay?' he asked.

'I just . . . got a little distracted,' she stammered.

Jimmy studied her face another moment. 'I'm beating Dad at Nintendo football,' he told her, seeming satisfied that she was all right. 'Forty-nine to fourteen at the half.' He pulled a few more Mallomars from the package on the table and hurried out of the room.

McKenzie grabbed the phone. 'Aidan?'

Dial tone. Aidan had hung up.

She hit redial. She wished she had told Aidan about the nightmare. But that had been just a dream. This had come over her while she was awake. And in such vivid detail. As if it had just happened. Or was about to . . .

Waiting for Aidan's phone to ring, she jerked her head in the direction of the clock. Ten till eight.

'Hullo?'

'Aidan! Thank goodness you're still there. Listen. Do me a really big favor, okay? Don't leave the house until I get there. There's something I need to tell you, and I want to tell you in person. And . . . and I love you like crazy and whatever you do, don't leave the house.'

'Why?'

'Just trust me, okay? Don't leave the house. Okay? Okay?'

Laughter crackled over the line. 'Okay, but this is Boz.'

'Who?'

'Boz. Remember me? Aidan's best friend. The three of us have spent hours hanging out together. I've got red hair, kind of a round face . . .'

Her heart was beating harder. 'Boz, hi, sorry. Where's Aidan?'

'He just walked out the door as I walked in. He went to pick up a video. But listen, don't let that stop you. I like hearing about how much you love me. Tell me – '

'Stop him! Get him! Now!'

'Hey, McKenzie, he'll be back in fifteen minutes . . . tops, and – '

'*Get him! Now!*'

'Sure . . . sure,' Boz agreed uneasily. 'Hold on.'

McKenzie waited, drumming the wall next to the phone. 'Come on!' she hissed, slapping the wall harder. Finally Boz got back on.

'You just missed him. Like I said, he'll be right back. You don't have to get so – '

McKenzie hung up. She scooped up her mother's car keys and raced for the door, grabbing her coat on the way out. She jumped into the car and pulled out sharply into the fast-falling snow. She glanced at her watch. Seven till eight!

'No need to worry,' sang Aidan as he sped down a side street in his parents' car. 'No need to care.' He thumped the steering wheel in time to the music. He knew he shouldn't be driving this fast on slick roads, but he wanted to make Movie Village before it closed. He was also anxious to get to McKenzie's. Maybe her line was just dead, but he'd feel better only after seeing for himself that she was all right.

He looked down at the clock on his dashboard: six till eight.

The ticking in her head was growing worse. McKenzie stepped on the gas and felt her car fishtail slightly on the ice. She gripped the ice-cold wheel. What route would Aidan take? He'd be coming from Hanover Street, that much she could count on. The quickest way to Movie Village was to cut through on Holland Drive. Aidan would be in a hurry. Yes, he'd take Holland for sure. If she could get to Holland Drive in time, she could cut him off. She braked sharply and turned without signaling. Behind her, a car honked furiously.

'Holland Drive,' Aidan muttered to himself as a reminder.

The minute hand on the dashboard clock notched forward: four till eight.

Just then, he saw a street sign flash by – Holland Drive! How could he be so stupid? He had missed it!

He hit the brake and took the next turn, onto Clark Street.

McKenzie pulled right out into the middle of Holland Drive, blocking both lanes. She put on her flashers. A lot of good they would do in this thick snowfall. But that was a chance she had to take.

She leaned over, staring out through her passenger-side window. The street was empty, deserted as far as the eye could see. She stared at the clock. Three till eight! Only a minute to go!

She forced herself to wait a few seconds more. 'C'mon! C'mon!' she prayed. But she had to face the facts – somehow she had missed him.

She backed up and yanked the wheel left. She floored it. In her head, the ticking grew louder.

'All right!' Aidan hit the wheel happily. At the far end of the street he could see the yellow, brightly lit marquee of Movie Village. The door opened and a few customers emerged. He might still make it.

Suddenly a car veered onto the street behind him, honking frantically. Was it honking at *him*?

Aidan hit the brakes. He stared back through the snow. A figure ran forward, waving her arms. Then a face appeared at his window, pounding on the glass. McKenzie!

'GET OUT!' she screamed, opening the door. She was tugging on his arm.

He fumbled for the catch on the seat belt.

'GET OUT!'

What was going on? He stumbled out of the car, one leg catching on the seat behind him.

Then he and McKenzie were stumbling away across the icy pavement. Just as —

The clock on the dashboard inside the car flicked forward.

Two minutes till eight.

Tick tick tick . . .

CHAPTER 4

February 3, 7:58 p.m.

And . . .

Nothing happened.

McKenzie stared across the street at the car in disbelief.

'What's going on?' Aidan gasped.

'There's a bomb in your car,' she told him.

'What!'

'At least, I thought there was.' She suddenly felt extremely confused, almost as if she were waking from a dream. Her vision had been so vivid, so detailed. She had seen it all. It had seemed real.

Aidan was moving back toward the car. She held his arm. 'Don't!'

'Where is it?' he asked, pulling free.

'The trunk, but – '

Aidan kept going. He fumbled for his keys with frozen fingers. There was nothing in the trunk except an empty oilcan, a jack, and a few old copies of *Sports Illustrated*.

'But I saw it!' McKenzie exclaimed. 'In my head. I saw it.'

'I believe you,' he told her gently. She could see he meant it. Aidan had no doubts about McKenzie's powers. He'd witnessed the effects too often for that. 'C'mon,' he said, 'follow me to the store. It's going to close any second. Then you can tell me all about it.'

She got back in her car, starting to feel a little better. The trunk was empty. That was the good news. She was also starting to feel very foolish.

When they got to Movie Village, the owner, Mr. Vitari, waved them away from inside. Aidan dropped to his knees in the snow and held out his hands, pretending to beg. McKenzie joined him.

Finally the owner unlocked the front door. 'You have one minute to pick out a tape,' he snapped.

They rushed down separate aisles, yelling out possible titles. Aidan finally rented a Van Damme kick-boxing movie. 'My brothers insisted,' he told her sheepishly.

Outside, she sat with him in his car for a

moment. She told him everything: the nightmare, the strange ticking sound in her head, the vision.

'Weird,' Aidan said.

'And then I saw the clock. It was two minutes till eight.'

He put his hand on her shoulder. 'It's over,' he told her in a soothing voice. 'We're fine.' He turned on the radio.

She fingered the crystal around her neck. She needed that safe feeling now. Her heart was still beating too fast. 'Aidan,' she began. 'Tonight turned out to be a false alarm. But something is happening. I just don't know what.'

'Well,' he said, 'then we'll have to do what we can to figure out what it is.'

'How can you stay so calm? I think someone may be trying to kill you!'

'Look, you thought the car recall caused your nightmare. Probably it'll turn out there's some other harmless explanation for this vision. Right?'

She kicked at the carpeted floor of the car. 'I hope so.'

He squeezed her shoulder. 'Guess what? The Shooting Stars broke up.'

The Stars were Boz's rock band. 'Aidan. Don't change the subject.'

'Wait a second. Listen. Boz and the lead guitar had a big fight over who gets to write the lyrics. Which means, I don't have to play keyboard on Wednesday nights. After I teach photo club, I'm free.'

'Sure,' McKenzie said. 'How long are you going to keep a free evening in your schedule?'

'Well, I thought this Wednesday we could go skating at the pond.' Aidan rubbed her neck. It felt so good. 'Mack?'

'Hmm?'

'Did you hear what I just said?'

She forced a smile. 'Skating at the pond.' But the truth was, she was growing distracted again. The radio. Aidan had it set to a rock-'n'-roll station. 'It was fate that we met,' sang the silky-voiced woman, 'and I can't get . . . you outta my heaaarrt . . .'

McKenzie turned to Aidan. 'Listen,' she said. 'It's the same song I keep hearing in my head. The song in my nightmare.'

'So?'

'So don't you think it's a strange coincidence that song would start playing now?'

'McKenzie – the song is a huge hit. It's playing everywhere, in the stores, in elevators, on every station. Of course, it's playing in your head. It's playing in everyone's – '

'Oh, yeah,' said the deejay as the song ended,

'it was fate that we met. And for those of you who haven't met your special someone, you better hurry up. 'Cause Valentine's Day is less than two weeks away.'

In a flash she remembered the deejay's voice in her vision. 'Love songs – on this special day we've got nothing but love songs, all day long.'

'That's it!' cried McKenzie. 'Valentine's Day!'

'Huh?'

'Aidan,' she said. 'It's going to happen on Valentine's Day.' She explained about the deejay.

'Okay,' said Aidan. 'So what's going to happen on Valentine's Day?'

She didn't answer. She couldn't speak the words: 'You're going to die.'

The darkness in Aidan's eyes told her he understood. He worriedly rubbed the crooked bump on his nose. 'When's Valentine's Day?'

'Uh . . . February fourteenth, which is . . .'

'A week from this Thursday.'

McKenzie didn't know who would want to hurt Aidan. But she knew this. They now had less than two weeks to change Aidan's fate.

CHAPTER 5

February 6, 3:48 p.m.
. . . tick tick tick tick . . .

'Hey,' Aidan said.

It was Wednesday afternoon. He was standing on the steps of the community center. Huddled on the step below him was Kevin Larsen. 'Your ride's late again?'

Kevin nodded. He had shown up at club today with a terrible black eye. As if that weren't pathetic looking enough, now his teeth were violently chattering.

'C'mon,' Aidan said. 'My car's over here.'

Kevin shook his head. 'I have to wait.'

'Kevin, it's ten degrees out here. A few more minutes and they'll have to pry you off these steps with an ice scraper.'

'My brother's coming,' the skinny little kid

said. It sounded more like a prayer than a state-ment.

Aidan pulled back his glove to look at his watch; the cold immediately rushed in at the exposed skin. 'He's twenty minutes late,' he told the boy. 'C'mon. I'll drop you and save him the trouble.'

Kevin still hesitated. He looked scared.

'What are you worrying about?' Aidan coaxed.

'What if he comes and I'm not here?'

'I'll take the blame,' Aidan assured him. 'Let's go.' He reached down to put a hand on the little boy's shoulder. It felt so tiny; he could feel the bone through the thin sweatshirt. Kevin got to his feet.

'Hang on one sec,' said Aidan as he fished in the pocket of his down jacket. He pulled out a felt-tip pen and the crumpled receipt from the rented Van Damme video. Leaning against the wall of the building, he hastily scrawled a mess-age: HAVE DRIVEN KEVIN HOME. AIDAN COLLINS. Then he ran back to the door and jammed the note into the groove between the glass and the metal doorframe.

'Okay,' he said, running back to the boy. 'Let's split.'

'Where do you live?' Aidan asked him once they were in the car. Now that Kevin had his hood off, his short brown hair looked choppy, as if he had cut it himself. He wasn't a good-looking kid. And the black eye he was sporting didn't help.

'Twenty-six Sumner,' Kevin answered obediently.

Sumner was close to Aidan's house. It was also a pretty run-down street.

Kevin's teeth were still chattering. Aidan reached down to make sure the heater was on high.

'By the way,' he said. 'How did you get that shiner?'

'I tried to catch a pop-up and missed,' the boy replied quickly, as if he had practiced his reply.

'Since when do you play baseball in the dead of winter?' Aidan questioned.

Kevin shrugged. 'We *were* playing,' he insisted.

Aidan still didn't believe him. But the boy's frightened eyes were asking him not to press. His scrawny body made those big green eyes look even bigger.

Exploring, the boy popped open the glove compartment. Inside was a packet of pink Kleenex and a small piece of knitting.

'It's my mom's car,' Aidan explained, glancing down to see what Kevin was examining.

'Sorry,' Kevin said. 'I wasn't snooping around. I just like to check stuff out.'

'Hey,' Aidan said. 'Quit apologizing so much, okay?'

'Sorry.'

Aidan shot a look at Kevin, but the boy was staring out the window. Three weeks ago, when Kevin's mom had first brought him to the class, she had told Aidan that his father had recently left home. She had asked Aidan to take special care of her boy.

Aidan wasn't usually judgmental, but something about Mrs. Larsen made him uneasy. She was a big woman, heavily made up, and her brittle blond hair looked like it had been bleached once too often. But that wasn't what bothered Aidan. There was something nervous, desperate even, in the way she spoke to him. He found her somehow unsettling.

As they approached the King Diner, Aidan slowed and parked on the shoulder.

'You know what?' he said. 'I'm really hungry all of a sudden. What about you?'

Kevin's eyes widened with surprise. 'Uh, no, not me.'

'Shakes? Burgers? Fries?'

'I got to get home.'

'It'll take five minutes.'

Kevin looked tempted, but he said, 'I better get home.'

'Why? What's the big deal about – ' It suddenly dawned on Aidan what the problem might be. 'It's my treat.'

A rare smile broke across the kid's face. 'Deal!' he said.

For a little boy, Kevin sure had an appetite. He ate half a plate of nachos, two cheeseburgers, one hot dog, two sides of fries (plus some of Aidan's), and a vanilla shake. 'They feeding you at home?' Aidan asked as Kevin slurped his shake dry.

Kevin nodded seriously.

'I'm joking,' said Aidan. He dipped a fry into the white container of ketchup. 'So you have what? Four brothers?'

'Huh?'

Aidan slapped his forehead. 'Wait a minute! That's *my* family. You have -?' He looked at Kevin expectantly.

Kevin burped. They both laughed.

'I know you have at least one older brother. How about sisters?' Aidan prodded again.

'Just my older brother.'

'Oooh.' Aidan grimaced. 'That's tough.'

Kevin frowned with suspicion. 'What do you mean?'

'Older brothers are a pain. Lucky for me, mine's in college. What's his name?'

'How would I know?' the boy asked, confused.

'No – *your* older brother. What's *his* name?'

'Oh. Craig.'

Aidan threw some more fries on Kevin's plate. He ate them immediately. 'How old is he?' Aidan asked.

'He's seventeen.'

'Oh, so he's a senior. Like me. How come I don't know him?'

Kevin answered with his mouth full. 'He dropped out.' Then he said quickly, 'You have a girlfriend?'

'That's kind of a fast change of subject.'

'Yeah, well, do you?'

'Kevin . . . you were telling me about your family.'

'Oh.' Kevin thought for a moment. 'I already told you.'

Aidan sighed. 'Well, listen. If you ever do want to talk about it . . .' He let the sentence hang. 'Yes,' he said. 'I have a girlfriend.'

Kevin let another smile slip, a small one. The news seemed to make him happy.

'And we're going ice skating later. How'd you like to join us?'

Kevin's smile spread into a grin, showing his crooked teeth and a mouthful of fries. 'Really?'

'Really.'

'Yeah!' He held out a small dirty palm, faceup. 'Can I borrow a quarter?'

'A quarter? How come?'

'I have to get permission from my mom.'

Aidan smiled and fished in his pocket for the coin.

Kevin placed the call from the restaurant pay phone. 'Craig? It's Kevin. Oh. You did?'

A look of instant terror had come over the boy's face. 'But I waited twenty minutes,' Kevin said meekly. 'Oh. I'm sorry.'

Aidan was standing a few feet away. He gestured for the phone, but Kevin shook his head. 'Listen,' Kevin said, 'the reason I'm calling . . .' He lowered his voice, and Aidan now heard only snatches of the conversation. But he could tell the talk wasn't going well. Kevin's mood was plummeting:

'. . . but I promise I'll do all my homework and clean up my room later . . .'

'. . . Yes, I'll be home in time to do all my chores . . .'

'. . . but I really want to go!'

By then, Kevin was crying. He was fighting it hard, but the tears kept coming. He turned his head away to hide them from Aidan.

'What's the problem?' Aidan demanded.

Kevin was sobbing now, making it hard to understand what he was saying. Aidan got the idea, though: Craig wanted him home. *Now*. Aidan asked if he could speak to Craig. Without looking at him, Kevin nodded.

'Craig? Aidan Collins. Hi. Listen, I'm sorry about the mix-up with the ride, but he was practically freezing to death out there. I left you a note on the door.'

'Yeah, well, it must have blown *away*,' said a surly voice. 'Because I didn't see no note. He was supposed to wait. He wasted my time.'

'Don't blame the kid,' Aidan said. 'I made him take the ride. I mean, his lips were bright blue, for – '

'I gotta go,' Craig cut him off.

'Wait a minute. I guess your brother told you that I want to take him ice skating. I could have him home by' – he looked at his watch – 'by six sharp, and – '

Craig wasn't paying attention. 'I found him, Ma,' he was calling. 'He's at some diner with his photography teacher.'

Then Craig got back on the line. 'Listen, save your breath, okay? He's not going. Not today. Not ever. Got it?'

'But – '

The line went dead.

Aidan stared at the phone in amazement. What was their problem? Mrs. Larsen had told him to take special care of her son. She had said that Kevin missed his dad; why wouldn't they want Aidan to spend some time with the boy?

Kevin was wiping his face with the heel of his palm and sniffling. Aidan put a hand on his shoulder. 'We'll go another time,' he promised, but he could tell that Kevin didn't believe him.

'How about this?' asked Lilicat. She modeled a see-through pink silk blouse with large, strategically placed pockets and a short black pleated skirt.

'That'll make him drool,' McKenzie promised. She was lying on Lilicat's bed next to a pile of clothes Lilicat had already tried on and discarded.

Lilicat studied herself in the full-length mirror on her closet door. 'I hate it,' she told her reflection, then disappeared back into her closet.

'Did I tell you about the good-night kiss?' she called.

'About a hundred times.'

'I can still feel it, though; that's the thing.'

Lilicat's twelve-year-old sister Gillian stuck her head in the room. She looked at the pile of clothes. 'I guess he asked her out again, huh?'

'Not yet,' Lilicat said, re-emerging with an armful of dresses. 'But he will. So don't jinx me.'

'What did *I* say?' Gillian asked.

She was only twelve, but Gill's recent growth spurt had caused her to grow taller than either McKenzie or Lilicat. She was also a pretty good dresser. Right now she had on a pair of raggedy black jeans, a white Gap T-shirt, and one gold earring. 'Why don't you borrow something from Gill?' McKenzie suggested.

'Forget it,' Gill said. 'My clothes aren't sophisticated enough for Lilith.' She used Lilicat's real name clearly just to be annoying.

Lilicat rolled her eyes. 'Listen,' she said. 'How about we go to the mall and shop for something. All my clothes bite.'

'Sure,' McKenzie answered, but without much enthusiasm. She had suddenly gotten that feeling again. Like Sunday night. That urge to call Aidan right away. And then the ticking – ever so faint – began again in her brain.

It turned out that Kevin lived in half of a two-family house that was badly in need of a new coat of paint. And a new color. Anything but dark brown. The windows were dark, dead looking; there was no car in the driveway.

'Mind if I come in?' Aidan asked. 'I want to talk to your mom for a second.'

Kevin looked terrified. 'I don't know,' he said, getting out of the car. 'Maybe that's not such a good idea.' He glanced nervously toward the house, as if he were afraid he was being watched.

'Why not?' said Aidan. 'Only for a second, I want – '

'You'll just get me in more trouble.'

'Trouble? Why would you be in any trouble for wanting to go skating?'

'Please don't come in,' Kevin pleaded. Then he closed the car door to end the discussion. 'Thanks for dinner!' He waved as he ran toward the house.

Aidan waited until Kevin let himself in the front door, using his own key. No one came to greet him.

A light flickered on in the kitchen, but it didn't make the house look any less foreboding. Aidan could easily imagine a vampire living within its dark, dreary walls. The house attached to Kevin's had no light, curtains, or shades. It looked totally empty. What a bleak place to live, he thought as he started the car again.

They had searched through three stores, and

51

still Lilicat had bought nothing. They'd been in the mall for over an hour. 'I think that's about it for me,' McKenzie said with a sigh as Lilicat shoved aside dress after dress in Pyramid Clothes. The plastic hangers clicked on the metal rack.

'One more minute,' Lilicat begged.

'That's what you said twenty minutes ago.'

'Well, if you would keep looking and find me something, then we could go.'

McKenzie sighed again and moved down the aisle, closer to the men's section.

'Mack?' Lilicat said.

'What?'

'You know who Kirk told me I look like?'

'Winona Ryder.'

Her friend spun around. 'You're amazing. How did you know that?'

'Lilicat. *Everyone* thinks you look like Winona Ryder. That's because you *do* look like Winona Ryder.'

Lilicat laughed. 'Thanks. But don't you see? It means Kirk thinks I'm, you know, attractive.'

McKenzie had moved farther away, to a rack of men's shirts. She reached up, flicking shirt after shirt aside. Lilicat might look hot in one of these, if she could find a small.

X-large. X-large. X-large. Medium. She

reached out and pulled an armful of shirts toward her.

That left a large gap.

And through the gap she found herself staring at a teenager on the other side of the rack.

His nasty green eyes bored into hers. His blond hair was crew cut. A skull earring dangled from his ear and a cigarette hung from his sneering lips. He even had on a frayed denim jacket.

It was the guy from her vision!

The face from outside her bathroom window.

Only this time he was even scarier than before. This time he was real.

CHAPTER 6

. . . tick tick tick tick . . .

'You!' McKenzie couldn't help herself. She screamed. Then she backed up, pointing a finger at the surprised teenager.

'What's your problem?' he demanded.

Lilicat was staring at McKenzie in horrified amazement. At McKenzie's scream a large, beefy security guard had emerged from the dressing area and now hurried toward them.

'I didn't do nothing,' the boy said, grinding out his cigarette in disgust. But when he saw the guard coming, he suddenly bolted for the door. As soon as he started to run, the guard broke into a run after him. McKenzie leaped to the side as the guard barreled past her like a pro-football fullback.

The guard caught up with the boy just outside the door. A few customers bustled outside to watch. Lilicat draped a protective arm over McKenzie's shoulder. 'You okay?' she asked. 'What happened? Did he hit you? Did he say something?'

Her concern caught the attention of the cashier, who hurried over.

'I'm fine,' McKenzie managed to tell both of them. 'Thanks.'

Outside, the boy was shoving free of the guard. 'Don't touch me!' he kept yelling. 'I didn't take a thing.'

'Just let me see what's in your pockets, and then you can go,' said the guard.

'Bunch of crazy people work at this mall,' the boy told the small crowd of onlookers. 'They ought to be fired. Some girl points at me for no reason. I never saw her before in my entire – '

'Just let me see what's – ' the guard repeated.

But the boy tried to run again. The guard caught him. There was a brief scuffle. Then the boy yanked a new, coiled black leather belt out of one pocket and threw it on the floor. The second the guard let him go, he ran off.

Moments later the guard returned to the store, shaking his head. 'Thanks,' he told McKenzie. 'Good eye.'

'Sure, I mean, you're welcome,' she stammered.

Frowning, the guard gave the black belt to the cashier.

'C'mon,' Lilicat said, taking McKenzie's arm, 'let's get away from here.'

They headed out of the store and looked for an exit. Standing by the revolving door that led to the mall parking lot, like a guard, was a large papier-mâché snowman. It held a sign: WINTER CARNIVAL IS COMING. DON'T FORGET THE MALL'S ANNUAL TOWN ANNIVERSARY SALE. 15% OFF ALL GOODS (AT PARTICIPATING STORES).

The snowman's button eyes stared at McKenzie blankly, hypnotically. Over its face her mind suddenly superimposed the smiling face of her man-in-the-moon alarm clock. In the next instant the moon's face dissolved into the image of the teenager at her bathroom window. The shoplifter she had just seen.

'Come on,' Lilicat urged, pulling on her arm.

Outside the mall, the mean gray sky hovered menacingly over the vast, empty parking lot. The air was freezing. There was no sign of the teenage boy. Or anyone else, for that matter.

'So what's *really* going on?' Lilicat asked as they approached her parents' car.

'I wish I knew,' McKenzie said.

Lilicat shivered. She got into the driver's seat and buckled herself in. She opened the window a crack.

McKenzie told her, 'I had a kind of nightmare about that guy, or someone who looks just like him. I didn't even see him shoplifting. It just freaked me out to run into the real-life version.'

Lilicat looked concerned. 'Oh, man! You and your visions. Sometimes I don't know how you can take it. You actually saw that creep in your head?'

McKenzie nodded and blew out a plume of steam. 'There's something about him that gives me the willies.'

'You're not alone,' Lilicat said. 'Listen, are you going to be all right? Want me to drive you home? I have to pick up Gillian and it's on my way. You can come back later for your car. Aidan will drive you back. Or I will.'

'Thanks. I'll be okay.' With a wave McKenzie headed for her mother's car. Patches of treacherous ice dotted the pavement like pieces on a game board. She kept her head down, pretending to pick her way through the ice, but in truth she didn't want anyone to see her face. The scene she'd made in the store still embarrassed her.

Lilicat had been right. Sometimes McKenzie felt that her special powers were more than she could handle. There were many times she wished she didn't have them at all. Life could be challenging enough without visions, precognition, dreams that came true, and all the rest.

When she was six, her parents had taken her to a psychologist. They had been alarmed by her violent nightmares, not to mention her sleepwalking. The doctor was totally stumped. He ran test after test. She *seemed* normal in every way. So what was the problem? The problem was that she had been born with these *powers*. And right now she felt as if her powers were about to drive her nuts!

She'd just have to relax, she told herself. She got into her car and started the motor, breathing slowly in and out, trying to take air deep into her lungs. Feeling better, she shifted into reverse.

The air in the car was stuffy, and smelled of Jimmy's moldy sneakers. She rolled down her window, letting in a blast of cold.

She had the window halfway down when a hand shot through the window and grabbed her around the neck!

He had her in a firm choke hold. She couldn't breathe, let alone scream.

'What's the big idea?' the boy from the store snarled. He leaned over so that his head was level with hers. 'That your idea of fun, trying to get people in trouble? Huh? Is it?'

The glowing red tip of his cigarette was only

inches from her face. She could see the white paper around the tip turning gray and black and receding slowly. Terror gripped her. She was just praying he would let her go.

'What were you thinking? That I'd get arrested?'

McKenzie jammed on the gas and the car shot backward. She felt the boy's hand fall away from her neck and thwack against the metal of the window frame. Then she saw him holding his hand and mouthing curses she couldn't hear. To get out, she had to drive past him.

She floored it, but he raced after her, trying to block her path to the exit. The car was too fast for him. He smacked the trunk of her car with his other hand as she went by.

'He was the guy I saw in my head,' McKenzie told Aidan. 'Exactly.'

It was later the same afternoon. McKenzie was propping herself against the bumper of the Collinses' car, lacing up her skates. 'My neck is still sore where he grabbed me,' she added as they hobbled on their skates from the car to the frozen pond.

Aidan looked furious. 'Let's call the police.'

Aidan was like that. Nonchalant about his own health and safety, but hyper about hers. If she so much as bumped her head, he was bugging her about going to the doctor.

'It's okay,' she said, hooking her arm through his. 'I'm sure I'll never see him again.'

Out on the ice, she grabbed his gloved hand and tried to spin him around. 'Whoa!' he cried, almost losing his balance. He clutched her wrist and they both went down in a heap. By then they were laughing. The sneering boy was beginning to go out of McKenzie's head, beginning to seem almost unreal.

The pond was crowded with skaters. Little kids, older kids, grownups, old people, and everyone was laughing, screaming, falling. Someone had set up a boom box on top of a car, and right now they were all skating to the upbeat sounds of Madonna. The air was freezing, unless you skated hard. It was just about impossible not to have a good time.

The sun was setting through the trees, glazing everyone's faces with a healthy red glow. McKenzie skated faster. Aidan tried a spinning jump. He went down again. She held out her hand to pull him up, and he pulled her down instead.

Soon she had forgotten all about her vision, and the guy at the mall, and anything else bad or scary.

'Feeling better?' Aidan asked an hour later as

they made their way through the crowd toward McKenzie's car.

She had her arm around him. Now she pulled herself around in front of him so that he had to stop. She kissed him full on the lips.

'Oooooh, we saw that!' teased some kids who were walking past through the dusk.

'I guess you are feeling better.' Aidan smiled.

'Thanks to you,' she said as they continued on to the car. 'I think this is one of those perfect moments. The kind you never forget.'

'Like a picture postcard,' he agreed.

In the distance the boom box's rock music suddenly died, breaking the mood.

Then McKenzie heard a match strike somewhere nearby.

A voice called, 'Look out!'

McKenzie saw a figure step up in the darkness and toss something that landed about fifteen feet away from them.

Whatever it was, it was on fire.

Startled, she watched it sizzle, and time seemed to stand still. McKenzie felt as though she was in some slow-motion scene. Her mind couldn't absorb this, couldn't make sense of it. She couldn't scream, nor could she move.

Then the sizzling thing exploded.

CHAPTER 7

. . . tick tick tick tick . . .

Bang!

The bomb exploded.

But it wasn't a bomb. Just a very loud fire-cracker.

'You okay?' At the last moment she'd shut her eyes and jumped back into Aidan's arms. Now he held her tight. McKenzie glanced up in time to see some kids running off into the twilight, laughing.

'Are you okay?' Aidan repeated.

'I think so,' McKenzie answered, still not grasping exactly what had happened. 'Just a bit stunned, I guess.'

'Those kids sure aren't very smart,' Aidan said.

He walked over to the site of the noise and

scuffed around in the snow. Then he bent down and picked up a charred piece of a small cardboard container. 'I thought so. It was an ashcan,' he said. He showed her the gray, shredded container. 'You know what this is?'

She nodded. 'Those big, loud firecrackers. The *Guardian* did a piece about them, and I wrote the editorial, urging the town to ban them, after that Wilson kid lost three fingers. A bunch of kids were actually making ashcans by themselves – with gunpowder! They *did* end up banning them, too, thanks to a certain prizewinning journalist. Guess it's time for another editorial.'

'Yeah, that might help. But you know, kids always get ahold of them somehow.' He peered into the darkness in the direction the kids had run. 'This happens every year,' he said. 'Right around the winter carnival.' He opened the car door for her. 'Looks like this year they're starting earlier than ever.'

February 8, 5:00 p.m.

Aidan tapped the paper with plastic tongs, making sure it stayed in the developer. A dark, scraggly tree branch slowly came into focus. It beckoned to him like a skeleton's arm.

It was late Friday afternoon. He was alone in

his basement darkroom. He was also alone in the house. The rest of the Collinses had dispersed to the usual variety of afterschool activities.

Aidan loved taking pictures, but developing them was even more fun. Being alone in the red glow of the darkroom safety light always made him feel cool, like an intelligence agent or something.

Behind him his automatic photo timer ticked softly. Its ticking slowed, halted — then the timer rang.

Aidan used the plastic tongs to lift the picture out of the developer and into the tray of water.

Then he set up the enlarger for the next print. A portrait of some kid. He set the timer for thirty seconds.

It made him happy printing these pictures for Kevin. He knew Kevin would be pleased. Maybe he could drop them off personally, before tomorrow's club meeting. It would give him an excuse to talk to Kevin's mother.

The more he thought about that black eye and the way Craig had sounded on the phone, the more worried he got.

The enlarger clicked off. The only light now came from the naked red safety bulb overhead. He put the newly exposed piece of paper into the tray of developer and moved to set the timer.

'Aidan? Are you in there?'

It was McKenzie. He had been too absorbed in his work to hear her coming down the basement stairs. But her voice was so familiar to him by now, it was almost never startling.

'Yeah! But turn the light off out there before you come in. I'm developing a print.'

When she came into the darkroom, the look on her face made him stop cold.

'Hey!' he said.

She didn't come toward him. 'I can't get him out of my head,' she said simply.

'Who?'

'The guy from the mall.'

'Should I be jealous?'

'Aidan, I'm serious. I don't know what's going on. But it's bad. I know it.'

'Come here.'

McKenzie stepped into his open arms, and he enfolded her in a long, hard hug.

'You didn't hear me calling?' she asked, her cheek on his shoulder. 'I guess not. Your front door was open, by the way. Tight security around here.'

'This is Lakeville,' he reminded her. 'Who locks their door?'

'You ought to,' she said, not letting him go.

'Not that I think you have something to worry about – until Valentine's Day.'

'Oh, that's comforting. I have a week left to live.'

She squeezed him harder. 'Please don't joke about it.'

'Sorry. Hey. Speaking of Valentine's Day . . .'

'Mm?'

'I was thinking about what I want us to do.'

'Oh, yeah?' she asked flirtatiously.

'Not that. The Avon is playing the most romantic movie of all time.'

'*Casablanca*?'

'*Bride of Frankenstein*.'

McKenzie groaned playfully. She had grown used to Aidan's love of horror movies. 'I figured we could see that,' he said, 'and then go to Destino's for dinner. I made reservations.'

'Destino's? Isn't that supposed to be kind of expensive?'

'Yeah,' he said proudly. 'But I can afford it. I've been saving my Gap money.'

He lifted her chin so that her lips were close to his.

'How do you stand it in here,' she murmured. 'It's so creepy. Your face and all . . .' He kissed her.

'Mmm . . . your face is red,' she continued, her voice softening, melting. 'And the smell in here. Those chemicals; it's like something is rotting.'

'Stop talking,' he told her, and kissed her again, harder.

He ran his hand fast all the way down her back. She let out a gasp. He pulled her closer to him, holding her as though he would never let go.

And all the time they were kissing, the picture continued to develop in its tray.

Aidan and McKenzie turned slowly in each other's arms. Then McKenzie looked down. She saw the picture. Her face contorted in fear.

'*Ow*!' Aidan yelped in pain. McKenzie's hands had tightened on his arms so hard that her nails dug into his flesh.

'Aidan!' she gasped. 'Look at that face!'

CHAPTER 8

. . . tick tick tick tick . . .

'What?' He followed her gaze.

Under the layer of clear liquid chemicals a face was materializing. A teenage boy. Crew cut. Small, burning eyes. A cigarette dangling from his lips. An earring shaped like a skull.

'Aidan,' she said, closing her eyes. 'Do you see the same picture I do?'

'Of course. Why?'

'Nothing. I just thought I might be going crazy.'

'Why?'

She opened her eyes again and stared down at the photo, mesmerized. 'Because this is the guy. The guy in my head. The guy from the mall . . .' She turned suddenly and gave Aidan a suspicious glance. 'Why didn't you tell me you knew him?'

'I don't. This isn't my film.' He lifted the picture with the tongs, placed it in the water tray, and looked at it closer. 'I'm printing it as a favor to a kid in my club. Kevin Larsen. I told you about him. His father left his mom. There's something so sad about him that I wanted – ' He was studying the picture.

'What?' asked McKenzie impatiently.

'I don't know. There *is* something about this face that looks familiar . . .'

She grabbed his arm again, as if to pull him away from the photo. 'Listen to me. Whoever he is, that guy is dangerous. I mean, he grabbed me by the throat! If you saw him in person, you'd know what I mean. He gives off really bad vibes.'

Aidan looked worried. He turned back to the photo. 'That's weird. Because all day I've been feeling like Kevin may be in some kind of danger.'

'If he's hanging out with this guy, he's in big trouble. Where are you going?'

'To call Kevin.'

McKenzie followed him upstairs, where he called from the kitchen. The phone rang five times.

'Hello?' a familiar voice answered. Aidan

recognized it from the phone call at the diner. It was Craig.

'Yeah, is Kevin there?'

Silence. 'Who wants to know?'

'This is Aidan Collins. Kevin's in my photography club at the community center . . .'

'Yeah, what about it?'

McKenzie stood close by, trying to hear both sides of the conversation. She watched Aidan's eyes for clues.

'I need to ask him about . . . a picture he took,' Aidan invented. Why did he need an excuse to talk to Kevin?

'He's not here, okay?' The voice was rude, surly, final.

'Well, do you know where he went? When he'll be back?'

'He's shopping with his mother. He won't be home for hours. *Okay*?'

Aidan pressed the receiver to his ear.

Because in the background he thought he heard something.

'What?' McKenzie prodded.

He shook his head. Was it the sound of a boy crying?

'Hey!' Aidan exclaimed.

The line had gone dead.

CHAPTER 9

. . . tick tick tick tick . . .

'If he's hurt that kid, I don't know what I'll
do,' said Aidan as they piled into McKenzie's
mother's car. 'Maybe it's none of my business,
but I can't just stand around and do nothing. I
mean, the kid's mother did ask me to look after
him.'

McKenzie didn't answer right away. Frightening images – her nightmare vision of the exploding car, the ghostly Peeping Tom – swirled in
her mind.

'What do you think I should do?'

Aidan's voice interrupted a thought forming
in her head, and she lost it. 'I don't know,' she
said, frustrated.

A car honked.

It was Aidan's mother and his brother

Patrick. Aidan rolled down the window. 'Hey, Mack!' Patrick yelled.

McKenzie smiled. 'Hi, Patrick. Mrs. Collins.'

Mrs. Collins waved.

'I'll be back in about ten minutes,' Aidan told his mother. She waved again and drove on.

The night was starry. Icy snow coated Lakeville, reflecting the streetlights and an almost full moon. McKenzie shivered at the sight of Kevin's house. The porch light was off; so was the streetlight in front of the house. The house itself looked almost completely dark. What were they doing here? Everything told her to get away. But if this boy was in trouble . . .

Aidan leaned past McKenzie to look out her window. 'Look!' he said.

A shape moved past the window of a dimly lit second-story room. Then it was gone. 'His mother?' he whispered.

'Let's go see what's up,' said McKenzie.

The doorbell didn't work. At least, it didn't make any sound that they could hear. Aidan knocked with his fist. No one answered.

'I just talked to him on the phone!' he said to McKenzie. 'So where is he?' He backed down the steps and craned his head toward the driveway. McKenzie didn't like being left alone on the porch, even for an instant. She knew it was irrational, but she felt as if the house might swallow her up while Aidan wasn't looking.

'Car's still here,' he said, returning. He pounded on the door this time. It shook in its frame.

'Let's go.' She stopped his hand. 'We'll come back later.'

He pulled his hand free and resumed pounding.

When the door swung open, he had his arm cocked to hit it again.

McKenzie stopped breathing. It was the guy from the mall. Just the sight of him made her legs tremble. She'd never seen such a malevolent expression on anyone.

'You going to hit me?' he sneered at Aidan.

Aidan lowered his fist. 'Sorry. My name's Aidan. I called a few minutes ago – '

The boy stared at McKenzie so openly that Aidan stopped what he was saying in midsentence. 'Hey, baby,' the boy said nastily. 'Can't stay away from me, can you?'

She tried to stifle a violent shudder.

'You must be Craig, right?' asked Aidan. The boy didn't respond. 'We wanted to see – '

Craig cut him off. 'Oh, yeah. Well, Kevin's still not here.' He started to close the door, but Aidan blocked his way.

'You wouldn't mind if I left him a note, would you?' Aidan asked.

Craig stubbed out his cigarette on the door-frame near Aidan's head. Gently, Aidan tried to push past him, saying, 'I'll just be a second.'

Craig didn't like being pushed, not even gently. He pushed back hard. 'Don't touch me, okay?'

'Okay . . . I . . .'

'You can leave a note. Then you can go.'

He opened the door. McKenzie and Aidan exchanged a glance as they went in. The foyer was dark. Craig made no move to turn on a light. Scattered newspapers and an open phone book lay on the floor. He ripped a page out of the phone book and handed it to Aidan.

Aidan slapped his pockets. 'Darn. Listen, do you happen to have a pen I could use?'

'I've got one,' McKenzie offered. Aidan's annoyed glance told her instantly she had made a mistake. How could she be so stupid? she berated herself. Aidan *had* a pen; he was just stalling for time.

Aidan moved farther into the house, but Craig blocked his way. 'Write your note,' he said menacingly.

McKenzie tried to take in everything she could. The peeling brown wallpaper, with its pattern of anchors and mermaids. The large, worn wooden staircase strewn with clothing. A grimy, overflowing ashtray. The dining room with dirty plates on the table and an empty cereal box on the floor. Clearly, good housekeeping was not high on Mrs. Larsen's list of priorities.

Aidan cleared his throat. 'Your mother's not around, by any chance?'

Kevin's mother . . . what if she were worse than Craig? thought McKenzie. She tensed, expecting some kind of monster to emerge.

'She's sick,' Craig said curtly, ending the discussion.

'That's funny,' said McKenzie. 'Before, you told us she was out shopping with Kevin. She must have gotten sick pretty fast.'

Craig was furious now. 'I lied, okay? Now I'm telling the truth! You got a problem with that?'

'No,' McKenzie mumbled, wishing Aidan would hurry up. He was writing very slowly.

'C'mon,' Craig snarled. 'Let's go.'

'What's your hurry?' Aidan asked.

Craig didn't answer. But McKenzie saw the look in his eye. He was losing what little patience he had. She felt sure when he blew, he would blow sky high. Finally Aidan folded the note and handed it to Craig. 'Be sure that he gets it.'

Craig smiled with mock sweetness. He had one hand in his pocket now. Did he have a knife?

'Listen,' Aidan said. 'I'm really sorry to keep bothering you like this. But it's important that I talk to Kevin. Is there any chance maybe we could wait for him for a few minutes? McKenzie? You have time?'

She wanted to run right out of the house, but she forced herself to nod. Aidan started moving forward again. 'You wouldn't mind if we hung out in here for a few – '

The hand that shoved Aidan back flicked out with lightning speed. 'Listen!' Craig snarled. 'I'm busy now, okay? I don't have time to *entertain* guests. So why don't you and your girlfriend – '

'Don't touch me!' Aidan warned him.

The hand flicked out again, pushing Aidan back another step. 'This is *my* house. And I – '

'I said don't – '

Another step. 'I don't want you in it!'

'Craig!'

The young voice stopped everyone cold. It came from the top of the stairs. Craig's head jerked back. 'Get in your room!' he yelled. 'I'll handle this!'

Kevin stood at the top of the stairs. As he advanced down one step, McKenzie saw his black eye.

'Who is it?' Kevin asked.

'I said, get back in your *room! Now!*'

'Kevin?' Aidan called. 'It's Aidan. Can I talk to you for a second?'

'No, you cannot talk to him for a second!' Craig's eyes were flashing. 'What is the matter with you? Don't you have ears?'

Kevin was far enough down the stairs now for McKenzie to see him clearly. He stood barefoot in worn jeans and a blue Hammer T-shirt. He looked terrified.

Craig pointed a finger at him like a gun. 'Back in your room. *Go!*'

'Kevin,' Aidan said, gently but firmly. 'Get your mother. Tell her I need – '

'Are you crazy?' interrupted Craig. 'You know she's sick. I'm not going to let you bother her. Now if you don't mind – '

He seized McKenzie and Aidan by the arms, pushing them toward the door.

But Aidan and McKenzie both pulled away.
'If I can just talk to Kevin for one minute,' Aidan told Craig, 'then we'll go.'

Craig was trembling with rage. But he nodded at his brother.

Kevin came down the stairs slowly. Aidan reached out to rest his hands on the boy's small shoulders. 'Hi,' he said. He smiled. Kevin's face was a mask of fear.

'If Kevin says his mom is sick,' he told Craig, keeping his eyes on Kevin's, 'then I'll be satisfied.' Kevin started to look at his brother, but Aidan squeezed his shoulders. 'Don't look at him. Look at me.'

Kevin stared right into his eyes. 'Is it true?' Aidan asked. 'Is she too sick to talk to me?'

'It's true.' Kevin smiled nervously after he said it, and for the first time McKenzie saw the boy's small, crooked front teeth. He's lying, she thought.

'There's your answer,' said Craig. 'Now get out.'

Aidan didn't let go. 'And she doesn't want to be disturbed?'

'Yes,' said Kevin. He was trembling.

'If you want her to bite your head off, just go upstairs and knock on her door,' added Craig. He laughed.

Aidan let the boy go. He doesn't trust me, he realized. Why should he? But what could he do to win that trust?

'Kevin,' he said, 'here's my home phone number.' He handed over the note. 'If you ever have any – '

Craig grabbed the paper from Aidan's hand, crumpled it into a ball, and tossed it playfully up in the air. 'Thanks,' he said. 'Now the party's over. Out.'

Aidan turned to go. So did McKenzie. But she couldn't move.

From where she stood, she could see across the hall to an old brown door. Its paint was badly chipped. She couldn't take her eyes from it.

'Mack?' Aidan said. 'You coming?'

I'm the only one who sees it, she realized. It was a lonely, frightening feeling. Because in her mind's eye, something behind that door had begun to glow bright red.

CHAPTER 10

February 8, 10:21 p.m.
. . . tick tick tick tick . . .

The car parked in the darkness down the street
from 26 Sumner Lane looked empty. It wasn't.

'Some date, huh?' Aidan whispered as he
slouched down low in the front seat. 'Don't say
I don't take you anyplace exciting.'

'I wonder if you can feel it when you're getting frostbite,' McKenzie whispered back. 'This
is crazy. Let's go home. I was wrong. I really
thought Craig would go somewhere after we
left. But he hasn't. And we haven't learned a
thing.'

Aidan slid up a few inches. There was no one
in sight. So far, the only thing they had seen
was Kevin going out.

Then they heard the sound of wood hitting

metal. At the other end of the street they could just make out the shapes of a few small boys walking in the direction of the car. One had a large, thick stick and whacked everything in sight – lampposts, fences, the icy pavement. Another kid darted toward him, trying to take the stick away. The bigger kid swung wildly, smacking the boy on the leg.

The boy went down. The group gathered around their fallen friend, pulling him to his feet. Then they moved on down the street, coming closer to Aidan and McKenzie. There were shouts.

'Look, there's Kevin,' McKenzie said as Kevin passed beneath the streetlight, tagging along reluctantly after the group of noisy kids. Even from this distance they could see the haunted look in his eyes. 'It's awfully late for him to be out, especially in this cold weather.'

Kevin went into his house. The porch light was off as usual; the house welcomed him with darkness.

'You know,' Aidan said after they had waited another twenty minutes, 'this is the part of following someone they never show you in the movies.'

'What's that?'

'The doing nothing part. The freezing to death part.' He sat up and blew on his hands, flexing his numb fingers. He turned the ignition key.

'What are you doing?' McKenzie asked.

'We're leaving. Tailing Craig was a good idea. It might have told us something about the scuzzball, but obviously the guy's not going out tonight.'

Just then the front door opened. Craig came out, the collar of his denim jacket turned up against the biting cold. He let the door slam behind him.

Then he circled to the driveway and out of sight. A motor churned. The beat-up yellow car swung into the street, the tailpipe scraping over the curb. When the car had almost vanished into the distance, Aidan pulled out after him.

Craig's car turned left on Millhouse, right on Cedar, right again on Crescent Hollow. Aidan stayed as far back as he could. 'It would help if there were some other cars around,' he said quietly.

'Just stay back,' McKenzie coached.

Aidan braked for a moment at Crescent Hollow, then turned. Up ahead the long street lay empty. Not a car in sight.

Aidan cursed.

'Where could he have gone?' McKenzie wondered. She closed her eyes and tried to imagine she was Craig, out driving . . . where?

She had no idea. Her mind felt as blank and empty as the dark street ahead. 'Why would he come this way?' she asked.

'The highway!' yelled Aidan suddenly. 'He's taking the shortcut to the highway!'

Aidan was backing up fast, skidding badly as he made an overly sharp turn onto Taber Avenue. Still no cars in sight. He floored it, speeding past the highway on-ramp sign. He came out of the ramp going sixty and merged easily with the sparse late-night highway traffic.

'See him?' he asked.

McKenzie was craning her head. 'No.'

Aidan quickly passed three cars, only to get stuck behind a long tractor-trailer. NO TAIL-GATING! warned the sign on the truck's back doors, only twenty yards away. NO PASSING ON THE RIGHT!

Aidan moved to the right.

'Aidan! Don't! What if he pulls over into – '

But he pressed the gas pedal almost to the floor, and the car surged forward. Just as –

The truck began to move right.

Aidan blared the horn. But the truck kept coming, pushing them off the highway onto the shoulder.

'*Aidan!*' McKenzie yelled.

The shoulder was narrowing, and they were

still only halfway past the truck. He jammed the gas pedal down one final inch, just as the shoulder ended. It was his only chance – Aidan shot in front of the truck. McKenzie bent over double, preparing for the collision. The truck's horn blasted in her ears. The collision didn't come.

Aidan kept moving left, out of the truck's lane.

Once they were safe, they drove in silence for a moment. 'We're fine,' he said at last.

McKenzie was still bracing herself against the dashboard with both hands.

'Guess I got a little carried away,' he added. He had moved back to the right lane but now swung to the left in order to pass the car ahead of them, when –

McKenzie said sharply, 'Aidan, it's him.'

The small yellow car was right beside them. It was Craig. They had caught up. If he so much as glanced their way, they were sunk.

But he was looking to his right.

'He's getting off!' McKenzie hissed.

Craig had swung off the highway onto the mall exit. Aidan hit the brakes, trying to exit right from all the way in the left lane. He barreled through the curvy off-ramp at far too high a speed.

When they got to the first stoplight, Craig's

car was going on ahead, turning into the deserted Lakeville Mall.

'Kind of late for the mall, isn't it?' Aidan observed.

The light changed and they followed Craig into the mall, parking the car in the shadows of a dark arcade of closed stores.

'Now what?' she said.

'Now we go around the corner. We also pray Craig and whoever he's meeting aren't right there.'

'What if they are?'

'Start thinking of a good reason why we came to the mall at this hour.' Aidan laughed nervously.

They got out of the car and hurried through an alley between stores. The high walls rose blankly on either side of them like a canyon.

They turned the corner and found themselves facing the vast sea of the back lot. It was lined with parking spaces and laced with icy snow. There were only a few cars. In the far corner, by a woody hill, two cars were parked. One was a yellow Lion.

In the distant darkness they could make out Craig, standing by the open trunk of his car. He was surrounded by a group of other teenagers.

McKenzie's heart pounded. One of the kids

gave Craig something. What? Money? 'What's going on?' she whispered.

'Shhh!' Aidan warned.

Craig and the other teenagers were looking around, anxiously checking to make sure that no one was watching them. Now one of the kids turned and stared right at McKenzie and Aidan.

Aidan pulled her back into the shadows.

'Did they see us?' McKenzie asked, poised to run.

'No,' said Aidan. 'They're still going ahead with their deal.'

'Deal? What kind of deal?'

'I don't know.'

McKenzie looked out to the lot in time to see Craig reach into his trunk and hand over several small packages. One of the teens, a tall, skinny guy, opened one of them. He nodded, seeming satisfied with the contents.

Now McKenzie knew what was going on.

She and Aidan were witnessing a drug deal.

CHAPTER 11

McKenzie turned to go, kicking an empty soda can. As it clattered across the ice, the tall skinny teen jerked his head in her direction.

'C'mon!' Aidan grabbed her by the sleeve.

They raced back to the car, weaving to avoid the sheer patches of ice. They got into the car, slamming the doors in their haste. Aidan fumbled for the keys, dropped them, and groped for them on the carpet below the brake pedal.

McKenzie kept a sharp eye on the building's corner. Any second now two cars would turn that corner. 'Hurry, Aidan!'

He turned the key. Nothing. The motor was totally silent. He tried again. And again. Then the motor whined softly. He pumped the gas, and the motor finally caught. Then he backed up fast, stopping just short of a pole. With a wail of tires, he pulled out of the mall.

The whole way home McKenzie rode with her head turned, watching for the small yellow car. It wasn't until they were at Aidan's house, standing outside in the crisp, freezing air, that she began to feel safe. The feeling didn't last long.

'I think we should call the police,' she said.

'And say what?'

'That Craig is a drug dealer who's abusing his little brother.'

'Wait a minute! Time out!' Aidan said, putting one hand on top of the other in a *T*. 'Are you sure?'

'Aidan – ' McKenzie let out an exasperated sigh. 'We just *saw* him with our own eyes – '

'Did you see any drugs?'

'No, not exactly . . .'

'He might have been selling old stereo equipment for all we know. We don't have the slightest bit of proof about drugs or anything else illegal.'

'I guess you're right.' McKenzie sighed. 'But what about Kevin? I just know he's being abused.'

'Right. But is Craig doing it? Maybe the mother hits him. We just don't know. Tomorrow's my club meeting. I'll get Kevin alone and ask him some questions then. I'll bet if I'm alone with him, he'll talk to me.'

'I hope so.'

'I care about him too, Mack. All I'm saying is, let's be sure first. If we're not careful, we could get him in even worse trouble.'

. . . tick tick tick . . .

It started so softly, it was more of a feeling than a sound. Then it got louder. The horrible ticking had begun again in McKenzie's brain.

'Aidan, I don't think we have a whole lot of time here. I think Kevin's in danger.'

'I told you I'd talk to him tomorrow.'

'I don't know. That black eye . . .'

'Not until we're sure.' As if to end the argument, he gave her a kiss on the lips and helped her into her car. Then he started walking across the street, toward his house.

'Aidan! I really don't think we should wait.'

He turned and walked backward a few steps. 'I think he'll open up if Craig's not there breathing down his neck.'

Since he was facing her, only McKenzie saw it. For a minute she thought she was in the grip of another vision. Then her eyes went wide. It was real!

It was happening so fast she couldn't get the words out to warn him.

A small yellow car had sped around the corner. Now it raced up the road at full speed – and it was heading straight for Aidan!

CHAPTER 12

'Aidan!'

Aidan turned. The car was almost on him.

He froze.

Then jumped.

He hit the pavement, stretching out his right hand to break his fall, just as the car rushed by.

The car did a half spin on an icy patch, then sped on.

McKenzie was out of her car in a flash, slipping and sliding on the icy street. 'Aidan!'

He rolled over with a groan, cradling his right hand with his left. His face was twisted into a silent scream of pain.

'Aidan, are you okay? Where does it hurt? Your hand?'

He nodded, wincing. She turned back. Up ahead, the small yellow Lion had screeched to a halt by the side of the road. Now a car door opened and slammed shut. Someone was getting out. Under the streetlight McKenzie saw that the person wore a black knit cap and a long black coat. A scarf was wrapped up to the person's nose, obscuring most of the face.

'Aidan,' McKenzie whispered fiercely. 'He's coming.'

In response Aidan gave a half grunt, then a sharp cry of pain.

But the same thought flashed through both their heads at once. Craig had just tried to kill him. Now he was coming to finish him off. The coat, hat, and scarf were a disguise in case anyone happened to witness the incident.

Footsteps approached quickly, but McKenzie didn't want to waste a second in glancing back again. 'Can you get up?' she asked desperately. Aidan reached up with his good hand and she grabbed it, pulling him into a sitting position.

But before she could help him to his feet, the figure was upon them. McKenzie was about to scream for help when the person spoke.

'Is he all right?'

McKenzie stared in disbelief. A sweet, frightened-looking woman in her forties pushed down her scarf and gazed at them, her eyes filled with concern. 'I'm so sorry,' she said. 'With that dark coat he's got on, I didn't see him until the last second. Then I couldn't brake fast enough on this ice.'

'We didn't see you coming,' McKenzie said, trying to remain calm. 'Aidan, what is it? You look awful. Is it broken?'

'My hand hurts,' was all he was finally able to say.

'C'mon,' she said, 'we've got to get you inside.'

The woman took one side, McKenzie the other as they helped Aidan to his feet. Even standing, he stayed bent over, cradling the hurt hand.

McKenzie turned to the stricken-looking driver. 'Can you wait with him a second? This is his house. I'm going to get his mother.'

The woman nodded vigorously. 'I'll be right back,' McKenzie told Aidan. As she rang the Collinses' buzzer, lights flicked on inside. She could see and hear people running down the front stairs. Then the porch light snapped on and Aidan's youngest brother, Milo, was staring out at her. The door swung open. Milo, Patrick, and Mrs. Collins all came out onto the porch. Mrs. Collins was pulling a coat on over her nightgown. 'Aidan – the car – ' McKenzie began, but Mrs. Collins was already past her, hurrying down the walk to Aidan.

The driver was apologizing to Mrs. Collins,

but McKenzie could see she wasn't listening; she was looking at Aidan's hand. Then she headed for the driveway and her car. 'C'mon, McKenzie,' she called. 'We're going to the hospital.'

Aidan insisted that McKenzie sign his cast before she went home. PROPERTY OF MCKENZIE GOLD, she wrote. She put a big red heart around it.

'Beautiful,' he said, holding up his right arm to admire it. He walked her to the Collinses' front door and flicked on the porch light with his good hand. 'Hey,' he remarked, 'you know, there is one good thing about all this.'

'Oh?'

'That vision of yours. You saw me driving. Well, now I can't. There's no way that nightmare can come true.'

She hugged him impulsively. He was right! She could feel the thick plaster shape of the cast as he rested it on her back. They kissed goodbye. Then her footsteps echoed loudly on the porch as she headed for her car. When she looked back, Aidan was watching from behind the front door. She knew he would watch until her car was out of sight.

He's still a little scared, she thought. After all, strange things had been happening ever since that dream of hers. But even as she said this to herself, she began to relax. Aidan was right. In this one weird way, it was good news that he couldn't drive for a while.

So what had that dream of hers been about?

Maybe it was about this brush with death – maybe that was what had prompted her awful vision in the first place. Not the car recall.

Yes, maybe it *is* over, she told herself.

Maybe now she could relax.

Maybe . . .

CHAPTER 13

February 13, 3:21 p.m.

McKenzie stood under the hot shower, letting the water pour down over her head.

She had gym last period, and now she was the last one in the shower room. The voices from the locker room had long since died out. She was alone.

She closed her eyes . . . the water pounded on her shoulders, relaxing her, soothing her. Her head dropped forward, and she rolled it lazily. The water drummed steadily in her ears. Steam rose around her, engulfing her in a hot wet . . .

Suddenly it wasn't so relaxing anymore . . . it was too hot – so hot she couldn't think or breathe.

She couldn't see a thing. Searching wildly, she finally grasped the hot-water faucet and twisted it with all her might. Anything to stop the hot water from beating down on her. But the shock of cold water didn't stop the burning feeling – the pain . . .

It's Kevin! He's crying! Craig is chasing him. Kevin races through the kitchen. He stumbles, reaches out to brace himself. The boy's arm slides across the glowing red burner on top of the stove.

He pulls away. He clutches his arm. Blisters form instantly.

McKenzie staggered back against the plastic shower wall. The sound of the shower filled her head. The droplets pounded her head at high speed. The sound became louder, and more forceful, like someone screaming in her ear . . .

Craig is shouting. He chases Kevin out of the kitchen, through the first floor of their house. He lunges. Kevin ducks away and darts through the archway into the dining room. He knocks into a chair. He's down.

Craig is on him now. He hauls the boy to his feet. He shoves him. Kevin flies backward. Smashes into the wall.

That awful peeling wall. The brown paper covered with anchors and mermaids. Craig raises his arm. 'I'll kill you!' he screams. 'I'll kill you!'

Kevin cowers. He puts his arm in front of his face.

His burned arm! Horrible, angry blisters.

'Stop, please!' Kevin pleads. *'Noooo!'*

CHAPTER 14

'No! Stop!' McKenzie screamed.

With the shower still pounding, she hurried out into the locker room, toweling herself as she went. She fumbled with her combination lock, pulled the door open, and yanked out her clothing. She began dressing as fast as she could, and yet it still seemed to be slow motion. She had to get to Kevin's house! Now!

She stepped into her shoes, trying to wiggle her feet into them while grabbing for her white silk blouse.

As she took a step across the wet, tiled floor she still felt burning hot. She looked at her arm. There was a red mark. It slithered across her skin like a snake. She opened her mouth in terror as all down her side blisters bubbled up. Then, right before her eyes, her livid red skin began to shrivel – as if from exposure to extreme heat.

The horror of the sight made her heart slam against her breastbone. Her breath caught in her throat. What was happening?

Half dressed, McKenzie ran toward the gym teacher's office. First aid, she thought. I need it now. Someone's got to help me. Oh, not know, not when Kevin needs *my* help . . .

'Help me!' she called out as she approached the office. 'I got burned in the shower!'

But no one was in the teacher's office when she got there. The rooms were dark and empty. She was hurt and alone. She had to get to a phone to call an ambulance.

She tried the doorknob again, twisting it hard. Then her glance fell on her arm. She looked again.

Then she fell against the door with relief. The burn was totally gone.

She was fine, but what about Kevin? Pushing back her dripping hair, McKenzie ran to her locker, hastily finished dressing, and ran out to the school parking lot. The winter sun was low in the sky as she slid behind the wheel of her mother's car and revved the engine for a quick start-up. Fat snowflakes plopped onto the windshield. Flipping on the wipers, she pulled out of the lot and sped all the way to Kevin's house.

She squealed to a stop in front of the foreboding house. She ran up to the porch and leaned on the bell. That was when she realized it was Wednesday. The photo club!

She was supposed to drive Aidan to the center, since he couldn't drive himself now. Kevin must be there as well.

McKenzie jumped back into the car. If Kevin wasn't at the community center, she would call 911.

First she had to get Aidan. Stepping on the gas, McKenzie drove back to the school. Halfway there her car started stalling out. Then she got caught in traffic. When she finally got there, McKenzie found Aidan pacing along the edge of the school parking lot. His hood was zipped up all the way so that it tunneled in front of his face.

'Where were you?' he said angrily as she leaned over and pushed the passenger door open for him.

She told him as she drove. His anger soon turned into fear. He wanted to drive back to Kevin's house or call the police. McKenzie insisted they try the community center first.

When they reached the center they ran, their footsteps echoing through the large empty hallway, to room 391.

Aidan flung open the door.

Jay had Nelson in a headlock. Bobby was chasing Stewart. One of the desks lay on its side. *Whack!* An eraser hit the wall just next to Aidan's head. It was meant for Stewart, but Stewart had ducked. Kevin cowered in the corner.

'*Hey*!' Aidan yelled, as loud as he could. That stopped the class cold.

McKenzie stared at Kevin. He stared back, his eyes wide with fear. On his right arm was a large white bandage.

Aidan was staring too. 'Kevin,' Aidan said, 'come out here; I want to talk to you.'

'Why me?'

'I'm not picking on you. I'm mad at all of you, believe me. The rest of you, I want this place cleaned up right now so we can start our meeting.'

He closed the door behind Kevin. The boy looked down at the ground. McKenzie knelt in front of him. 'What happened?' she asked gently.

'We were waiting and waiting, then things just started getting a little out of hand.'

'No, not in there. At home. What happened to your arm?'

Kevin didn't look at the bandage. It was as if he was scared to. He shrugged and bit his lip.

'You can tell us,' McKenzie coached.

'I had an accident.'

'When?' Aidan asked.

'About an hour ago. Right before I came over here.'

'What happened?' McKenzie said again.

A look of terror came into his eyes. 'I burned myself,' he said.

'How?'

Kevin's fear was increasing visibly. 'Mack,' Aidan said quietly. What he meant was, 'Let me.'

'Kevin,' he said, 'we just want to help.'

'My mom told me not to use the stove by myself,' he mumbled, looking down again.

'But you did?'

'Let's see.' McKenzie reached for the boy's arm, but he jerked it back fearfully.

'It's nothing,' he insisted. 'I'm okay.'

'Craig did this to you,' she said.

He looked like he was about to cry. 'No! I'm telling you, it was an accident. I wasn't looking where I was going, and – '

'Craig's never hurt you?' she pressed.

'No.' He smiled nervously at Aidan as if to say, 'You believe me, don't you?'

'Okay,' Aidan said, putting his hand on his shoulder. 'Let's get the club started.' He opened the door, and Kevin went back to his seat.

'You'll pick me up after?' he asked McKenzie.

She nodded as he closed the door. But she didn't walk away.

It was as if she could see Kevin through the closed door. She could feel his heart pounding.

He was still afraid, she was sure. But why was he so afraid of them? What would Craig do to him if he thought that Kevin had told on him?

She knew they were going to find out.

Soon.

Tick . . . tick . . . tick . . .

CHAPTER 15

When she walked into the kitchen, her father turned toward her from the stove with a greasy metal spatula raised high in triumph. He was wearing his big blue apron, the one that said DANGER! DADDY'S IN THE KITCHEN!, a Father's Day gift from her and Jimmy two years ago.

'Your father's a genius,' he told her, beaming.

'Why? What did you do?'

'What did I do? Can't you smell it? I cooked us all a healthy dinner from the *Nature's Way* cookbook.'

'You're in a good mood,' she said with a smile.

'I am at that,' agreed Shelby. 'And you will be too once you've sampled *this* feast.'

'What's that horrible smell?' Jimmy asked as he slouched into the room.

'That horrible smell,' Shelby told him, 'is coming from the delicious veggie burgers your father is making for you.'

'Where's Mom?' Jimmy asked, shooting a worried look at the stove.

Shelby raised an eyebrow. Then he turned back to the skillet. 'If all is going according to plan, your mother is closing a deal on the Alexander house even as we speak. She'll be home soon.'

McKenzie pulled a two-liter bottle of Sprite out of the fridge and sat down heavily at the kitchen table. The burgers did smell awful, but it still felt great to be home, *safe*. She felt safer in this room than she felt anywhere in the world, especially when her dad was around. She took a swig right from the bottle.

'McKenzie's drinking from the bottle!' yelled Jimmy. Shelby turned fast enough to catch her. 'McKenz –!' he warned.

McKenzie plunked the soda back on the table and chased her brother out of the room. She caught up with him in the living room and threw a couch pillow at him just as Joanne Gold came bustling in, along with a rush of freezing air.

McKenzie could tell at once that the sale had

gone through, because Mrs. Gold didn't seem to notice that her children were fighting. 'Hello, hello,' she sang, glancing at the mail on the hall table. 'I did it!' she called to Shelby as she hung up her overcoat.

'Atta baby!' he called back from the kitchen.

'Atta baby, Mom!' Jimmy echoed, running to greet his mother and punching McKenzie on the way.

Mrs. Gold gave Jimmy a hug, looking over at McKenzie as she did. 'No congratulations from my only daughter?'

'Congratulations, Mom. That's really great,' McKenzie said quickly. 'Sorry, I was just thinking about something that happened today.'

From the smell in the air, it was clear that the veggie burgers had begun to burn. 'I think we better eat this right away,' Shelby called.

Joanne rolled her eyes, and McKenzie laughed. 'Oh,' her mother remembered. 'Someone left you a valentine this morning.'

'This morning?'

'It was on the porch when I came back from dropping off Jimmy at school. I put it on your bed.'

'Lover boy left a valentine! Lover boy left a valentine!' chanted Jimmy.

McKenzie felt a rush of warmth. Aidan was so great. But how had he found the time to deliver a present – especially when he couldn't drive?

She ran up the front stairs. Blue was scratching outside her closed bedroom door, trying to get in; and he raced inside when she opened the door. The package sat on her pillow. Blue jumped up on the bed and started sniffing at it, meowing.

McKenzie patted Blue and laughed. 'Sorry, kid. This is *my* valentine.' She shooed Blue away and picked up the box, smiling with anticipation. The box was large and wrapped in shiny pink foil. The card read, *To My Number One Valentine*.

She ripped off the wrapping.

Inside was a white box. She eagerly pulled open the flaps.

The white box was packed with green tinsel. She pulled out a few handfuls, then reached in again. She felt something coarse, bristly, and strangely cold.

She pulled it out.

Two beady black eyes stared at her.

She was holding a dead rat. A penknife had been jabbed deep into its gray, bloody back. Tied around the rat's neck was another note, which read, *Stay away. This means you.*

She leaped to her feet. But her hand would not let go.

She let out a bloodcurdling scream.

Blue raced out of the room. She heard the sound of her family calling. She could hear people running, footsteps scrambling up the stairs. She dropped the rat on the bed and flipped the spread over it, hiding it just as Shelby rushed into the room.

'*What?*' he gasped.

'Oh, Dad,' she said shakily. 'I'm sorry. Did I scare you?'

'No,' he said. 'I'm used to you screaming at the top of your lungs as if you're being murdered. It's music to my ears.' He sat down on her desk chair.

'Aidan wrote me the most gorgeous valentine letter. I guess I got carried away.'

'I guess so.' He rubbed his face.

Then he stood up. 'Well, glad to see the old heart can still handle a stress test.' He headed for the door. 'Your mother just put the burgers down the disposal. The pizza should be here in about fifteen minutes.'

McKenzie forced a laugh. She closed the door behind him. Then with a quivering hand she gingerly pulled back the spread, half hoping to find the rat gone. Blue had jumped back onto the bed, his nose twitching. She pushed him away.

The dead rat looked smaller now, and a little less scary.

She reopened her bedroom door and tossed Blue out. The hall phone was still in her room – the extension cord stretched to just inside the door. She bent down to pick it up, but before she could touch it, it rang.

She jumped. It was as if the phone had yelled at her when she reached for it. For a moment she felt like Alice in Wonderland. The world seemed animated, alive with all sorts of terrifying surprises. And nothing was what it seemed to be.

The phone rang again. An impatient, insistent ring.

She answered and heard her best friend sobbing.

CHAPTER 16

'**Lilicat! What happened?** What's wrong?'

Lilicat answered with another sob. Then the receiver clunked down, and McKenzie heard the muffled sounds of Lilicat blowing her nose. When she got back on the phone, she said, '. . . Kirk . . .'

'Kirk what?' McKenzie asked. 'What did he do?'

'N . . . n . . . nothing,' Lilicat whimpered. 'That's the problem. He doesn't want anything to do with me.'

Lilicat blew her nose once again, and McKenzie slumped against the wall with relief. She knew she should be sympathetic, but she was finding it almost impossible to focus on what Lilicat was saying. All she could think of was getting the blood-splattered dead rat off her bed.

'I got over the fact that he never asked me out on a second date,' her friend sniffled. 'So then I'm talking to Judy Jerome to tell her about the extra cheerleading practice for the wrestling meet. We're getting together tomorrow night at seven to – '

'Lilicat, what about Kirk?' McKenzie moved the phone as far away from her bed – and the rat – as it would go.

'I'm getting to it. So then Martina tells me that Kirk has been going out with Mallory Moore.'

McKenzie wanted to be a good friend, but she was getting impatient. Someone had sent her a dead rat. A little boy was in danger. Tomorrow was Valentine's Day – a day she'd been dreading for weeks. 'Listen, Lilicat, Kirk wasn't as wonderful as – '

'It gets worse,' Lilicat interrupted. 'Mallory told Martina that Kirk told her that I'm – ' She started to cry again.

'That you're what?'

'. . . a terrible . . . kisser!'

'No! What a lousy thing to say. That just proves he's a jerk.' As McKenzie spoke, she glanced at the rat. A shudder of disgust ran through her. 'Listen, I'm really sorry, but I gotta go. I promise I'll call you back later. Just remember that it's his problem, not – '

'It just hurts so much. It's like a knife in the back.' McKenzie couldn't help glancing once more at the rat.

'Lilicat – I gotta hang up right now.' She pressed down on the receiver button without waiting for Lilicat's good-bye. Then she gingerly picked up the comforter on her bed, with the rat inside. She shook it out over her wastebasket. It sickened her to see the dark, dead creature falling through the air. She ran outside to empty the wastebasket into the trash. As soon as she was back inside she washed her hands five straight times. Then she sprayed her comforter with Lysol. Then she picked up the phone and speed-dialed.

'Hello?' Aidan answered.

'What are you doing?' McKenzie asked.

'Calculus,' said Aidan.

'Have you talked to Kevin or anything?'

'No.'

She told him about the valentine. 'It has to be from Craig,' she said.

'That's it! He's gone too far!' Aidan cried, furious. 'I'm going over there right now and I'll set him straight.'

'Aidan, don't,' said McKenzie. 'It wouldn't solve anything. Besides, you're not exactly in great shape to do that.'

'Oh, right. You're right. Damn! I can't wait to

get this cast off. Listen, you want me to come over?'

'Uh . . . Aidan . . . you forgot again. You can't drive.'

'I'll have Boz pick me up.'

'That's okay. I'll be all right.'

'Are you sure?'

'Yeah.' But when she hung up, she saw that her hands were trembling.

That night she woke from a dreamless sleep with a feeling of terrible dread. The only sound in the room was the ticking of the clock. She could see the glowing moon face, grinning at her in the dark. Three in the morning.

What had awakened her? She listened. The house was quiet. She got out of bed.

She realized she'd fallen asleep in her clothes. She undressed, letting her clothes drop to the floor. Then she put on her red nightshirt.

Outside her window, snow was falling. It covered everything – lawns, cars, trees – like meringue on a pie.

She touched her hand to the cold glass. It was peaceful outside, the snow falling so steadily, so silently. Falling, falling . . . falling . . . falling. . . .

Aidan is driving down a street. Too fast. Outside, snow falls silently.

Tick tick tick tick tick . . .

He looks so tense, so worried. There is a Band-Aid on his left cheek. Why? What happened to him?

'Love songs,' croons the deejay. 'On this special day we've got nothing but love songs, all day long.'

The dashboard. The clock. Two minutes till eight. No time left.

As the car rushes past the streetlights, they light up the inside of the car with a series of flashes – on, off, on, off. In the light she can see that he has only one hand on the wheel. The cuff of his shirt is bright red. But why one hand? He never drives with just one hand.

One hand. The other hand is in a cast!

TICK TICK TICK TICK TICK. . . .

The ticking stops for the briefest of seconds.

And then . . . a blinding white fireball . . . shattering glass . . . the screech of tearing metal . . . a tower of flame.

Glass rains onto the street.

There is no way anyone can survive such an inferno.

Aidan!

'Wha – ?' Aidan picked up his telephone.

'It's me.'

'Oh. Just a sec – ' There was a long pause.

His voice sounded clearer when he got back on. 'What time is it?'

'Three.'

'Wow.'

'I just saw it all again.'

'Mack – '

'You drive with one hand. You wear a Band-Aid on your left cheek, a red shirt.' She was out of breath. 'You drive with one hand,' she said again.

There was a long pause. 'Wait a sec. I don't have a Band-Aid on my left cheek.'

McKenzie sighed again and again. 'Well, keep it that way. And don't wear a red shirt tomorrow. Just because it's Valentine's Day, you don't have to wear red. Okay?'

'Deal,' he said.

'Aidan,' she said. 'I feel like I'm going nuts.'

'Don't panic,' he said shakily. 'Everything's going to be okay.'

'Sorry I woke you up,' she whispered.

'Happy Valentine's Day,' he said grimly.

McKenzie watched the minute hand move forward. One minute to go.

She was sitting up in bed, holding the alarm clock in her hand. She hadn't been able to fall back asleep since three. The moon face now smiled brightly. Then the clock hand shifted:

six thirty. The alarm clock exploded with noise.

It was Valentine's Day.

At her place at the kitchen table lay a silver heart. Her father had jigsawed it out of aluminum down in his basement workshop. She smiled fleetingly and pocketed it; then she sloshed down some hot chocolate, scribbled a note of thanks, and hurried out.

The snowfall had continued heavily all night. The plows were out. She drove to Aidan's as fast as she could, listening to the school cancellations on the radio. Please let us have a snow day, she prayed. Please!

That way Aidan would stay home, safe.

'Lakeville High and Junior High will be open on a normal schedule,' the announcer said. What would it take for their principal, Mr. Pevny, to declare a snow day, she wondered irritably. She wrote a headline in her head: AVALANCHE, TORNADO, AND EARTHQUAKE ALL HIT LAKEVILLE ON SAME DAY! HIGH SCHOOL TO STAY OPEN, SAYS PEVNY.

Aidan was standing in front of the open fridge drinking out of an orange juice carton when McKenzie walked into his kitchen. He wore yellow sweatpants and no shirt. His sandy hair was even messier than usual, and he looked as if he was still half asleep. He stared at her blearily.

'Listen,' she said, 'what do you say we don't go to school?'

He pulled out an apple and took a bite. 'Why? School's on.'

'Just to be safe.'

'McKenzie, I'm not afraid of school.'

'What about what I saw last night? Aidan, you know – you *know* – my visions come true.'

Aidan held up his right hand, showing her the cast and wiggling his thumb. 'Remember this?'

She sat down. 'I already told you. In the vision, you drive with only one hand.'

'Look, I'm scared too. That's why I'm not driving today, no matter what.'

He closed the fridge and turned toward her. Her jaw dropped. Taped to his left cheek was a pink Band-Aid.

'What is *that*?' she asked.

'The power of suggestion,' he told her. 'I was shaving this morning and I kept thinking of what you told me last night. So I tried really hard not to cut myself shaving. I tried so hard not to that I did.'

'But don't you see? The snow, the one hand, the Band-Aid – it's all coming true. And if it does come true . . .'

They both knew how to finish that thought. If it did come true, Aidan would be dead.

'What about the red shirt?' Aidan told her. 'I don't even own a red shirt.'

Just then, Mrs. Collins shuffled into the kitchen in her robe and slippers. She was carrying a shopping bag. 'McKenzie!' she said with a smile. 'You're here early.'

She kissed Aidan's cheek. 'Happy Valentine's Day,' she told him. She reached into the bag. 'I saw these on sale in the store yesterday, and I couldn't resist. I got one for each of you.'

She held out the package. 'A little valentine gift for one of my favorite valentines,' she said.

'Thanks, Mom.' Blushing, Aidan gave his mother a peck on the cheek.

He put the box on the kitchen table, fumbling as he tried to open it with one hand. 'Here, I'll help you,' McKenzie offered, steadying the box.

Aidan lifted the lid. The color drained from his face.

'Oh no!' cried McKenzie.

CHAPTER 17

February 14, 8:42 a.m.

'What's the matter?' Mrs. Collins asked. 'Red for Valentine's Day. I thought it was cute.'

Aidan hooked an arm over his mom's shoulder and pecked her cheek again. 'It is cute, Ma. Thanks.'

McKenzie didn't have to look in a mirror to know she was as pale as a ghost. Mrs. Collins looked at her, clearly worried.

'Sorry,' McKenzie stammered. 'I always get a little wired on Valentine's Day. It's just a weird day for me.'

At that moment the doorbell rang, and Aidan insisted his mother get it. It was the florist, he knew; he and his brothers had chipped in for two dozen long-stemmed roses.

McKenzie watched Aidan closely.

'Don't worry,' he told her. He looked at the red shirt. 'I won't wear it. I promise.'

'Did James turn in his minutes from the student council?' asked the *Guardian*'s news editor, Carol Ann Licht, later that day.

McKenzie shuffled through the papers on her desk and handed them over. 'Pretty boring,' she commented.

'They always are. All right, Mack. I'm taking off. Have a Happy Valentine's Day.'

'I'll try.'

Carol Ann hesitated. 'Don't stay too late.'

'I won't.'

Then the door closed, and McKenzie was alone in the *Guardian* office. Usually she liked working by herself at the school paper. Today, though, was different.

The phone rang an hour later. 'It's me,' Aidan told her.

'You got home safe?'

'Do I sound like I'm in trouble? Boz drove. So when are you coming to pick me up?'

'Aidan, I already told you to cancel the reservation at Destino's.'

'Okay,' he agreed. 'The roads are pretty icy . . . and anyway, I have a backup plan.'

'What's that?'

'You bring me the ingredients and I'll make you my special homemade pizza.'

Aidan was a terrible cook. He could ruin a bowl of Cheerios. But for some reason, he could make a great pizza.

'Deal!' McKenzie answered. 'I'm leaving now.'

She hung up and checked her watch. It was already almost five o'clock. Only three hours and two minutes to go until . . . until what?

With a shudder she laced on her tan duck boots, got her coat, and turned toward the door.

The door. Something was strange about it. Before her eyes it began to blur, change. The green paint took on a faint glow. It grew darker and darker, until it was a sickly brown.

Suddenly she was looking at another door altogether. The brown door. The door at Kevin and Craig's house.

The door began to glow bright red.

The pain hit her so hard that she doubled over. It was as if she had been kicked in the stomach. But she was all alone here. Where had the pain come from?

Suddenly she knew what was happening.

She could see it as if she were there.

It was Craig.

Craig was beating up Kevin.

McKenzie supported herself on a desk. 'Uh!'

Another blow hit her side. Tears of pain sprang up. This was unbearable. She had to stop it!

In the next moment the pain was gone. The beating was over. She didn't even feel bruised. She felt cold.

Had Kevin passed out?

He could be bleeding inside. He needed a doctor.

McKenzie ran to the empty hallway. She had to get to Kevin. Now.

CHAPTER 18

February 14, 6:21 p.m.

McKenzie slammed her hands against the steering wheel in frustration. Getting to Kevin's was taking forever! High piles of snow narrowed the streets. On some roads cars had spun into ditches or gotten stuck. As far as she could tell, traffic was backed up for about a mile.

As she drove slowly past yet another stranded car, she was dimly aware of romantic music playing in the background. She must have left the radio on; she didn't look down to check. She had to keep her eyes focused on the white road in front of her.

The wind howled, but the snow had stopped. Good, she thought. It had been snowing in her vision of Aidan. Of course, it could start again, but for now no falling snow was a good sign.

Maybe since Aidan was staying home, they had somehow changed everything. She hoped so.

McKenzie pulled up in front of Kevin's house, shut off the motor, and jumped out.

There was no car in the driveway. No light on inside. It was hard to run through the drifting snow.

No one answered her knock. But when she tried the knob, she found that the front door was unlocked.

'Kevin?' She stamped the snow off her boots and took a step into the dark foyer. 'Kevin!'

She moved from room to room, calling his name. At any moment she expected to spot him lying somewhere, unconscious. She was also braced for someone to leap out at her. She circled through all the downstairs rooms. No one there.

Back in the front hall, the staircase seemed to beckon to her, inviting her up. She slowly approached.

I've got to see if he's okay, she told herself. I've got to. She said it again, because her feet were telling her to turn and run.

The upstairs hallway was as much of a mess as the first floor. She tripped over a barbell and into an open doorway. She was in a tiny bedroom with nothing in it but a single bed, a rickety desk, and a poster of Arnold Schwarzenegger in *Terminator 2* on the wall. Tacked to the door were several amateur shots of trees and the portrait of Craig that Aidan had developed. So this was Kevin's room.

'Kevin?' Still no answer.

She knocked at the next door, then opened it. Inside was the worst mess she had ever seen. Everything in the room was on the floor: mattress, more barbells, skateboarding magazines, a plate of cold pizza, overflowing ashtrays. Craig's room. She moved on.

There was one more door. It was tightly closed. 'Mrs. Larsen?' she called gently as she knocked.

She got no response and tried the knob. It was open.

Stepping inside, she was sure the room would be empty. But it wasn't. Mrs. Larsen was lying in the bed, her face turned to the wall.

The air was musty. McKenzie knew right away that it was true after all. Mrs. Larsen was ill. Seriously ill.

'Mrs. Larsen,' McKenzie started, 'I'm sorry to bother you, but I'm worried about your son, Kevin. I wanted to check if he was all right, because – Mrs. Larsen?'

Mrs. Larsen hadn't answered, hadn't even moved.

'Mrs. Larsen? Mrs. Larsen!'

McKenzie shook the woman's shoulder, turned her over.

The face she saw turned her blood into ice –

Mrs. Larsen had red cheeks, a blond wig, and no eyes – no eyes at all.

CHAPTER 19

McKenzie stumbled backward. Mrs. Larsen was just a mannequin. Her cracked red cheeks were like some demented doll's. Her wooden mouth, painted bright scarlet, hung open in a vapid smile. Her empty eye sockets seemed to stare right at McKenzie as she backed out of the room.

McKenzie bolted, clattering down the steps two at a time.

She wanted to run right out of the house. Then she noticed the basement door. The brown door, its paint slightly chipped. It was ajar.

Her chest was heaving. She felt faint. You've got to go down there, she told herself. *Go! Go!*

She moved closer. Reached for the knob.

There was a light switch on the wall, just inside the door. She flipped it on.

A long flight of rickety wooden stairs led down at a steep angle. She had to be careful not to trip as she made her way down the steps, one at a time. It was cold down here, even colder than the rest of the house. And it was cluttered. Boxes covered the floor. A thin green blanket covered the windows.

An old sheet hanging from a clothesline partitioned off the back of the basement. She made her way over to the sheet and lifted the edge.

Behind it she saw a lab of some kind, a factory. Jars of white powder were everywhere.

'He really *is* making drugs!' she exclaimed. 'There must be thousands of dollars worth of stuff back here!'

She had to get out of the basement – quickly.

She had started making her way back toward the stairs when suddenly the door at the top of the stairs slammed shut.

She froze.

Someone had turned off the lights.

CHAPTER 20

McKenzie stumbled toward the stairs in pitch darkness. She bumped into something – a lamp? There was a crash. She flinched, then kept on.

Her hand closed around something hard. The banister! She felt the first step with her foot. She began to climb, hugging the wall with her hand. The tilt of the stairs seemed much steeper in the dark; she felt as if at any second she would fall. She took the second step. The third.

Then the lights flicked back on. She blinked, blinded by the sudden glare.

Craig stared down at her from the top of the stairs, a cigarette dangling from his lips. Curls of smoke rose toward the ceiling.

'So you met Mom,' he said, his eyes flashing angrily. Her head turned instinctively, surveying the room for possible escape routes. There were none.

'She's a doll, isn't she?' he continued. Then he laughed, a long, rasping laugh that sounded close to a howl of pain. She'd heard that laugh before, that night in her bathroom, when she saw the face at her window. Craig's face.

The only way out was to get past him somehow. Talk to him, she urged herself. 'Where's your real mom?' she asked.

'Oh, here, there – who knows? Ever since *Dad'* – he nearly spat out the word – 'left us, Mom hasn't been around that much. She takes off for weeks at a time. Which is just fine with me, let me tell you. She's a pain in the butt.'

He smiled.

'Craig, I didn't mean to snoop – ' McKenzie began, trying to cover the fact that she had just cautiously put one foot up on the next step. If he kept on talking, maybe he wouldn't notice that she was moving slowly upward.

And Craig, still smiling, kept talking. 'She really makes me mad sometimes. That's why I like it when she's gone. Gives me plenty of time for business. Sometimes I even pretend to be her on the phone, just to keep people like you off our backs. Oh, and the dummy – I mean the one you saw, not Mom – she's there to throw off the social worker who comes snooping around every once in a while.' He cocked his head and smiled. 'Sorry, Mom isn't feeling well. Yep, still sick. Go see for yourself, but don't wake her.' His false smile dissolved into a snarl.

McKenzie was on the fifth step now. She kept her eyes locked on his. 'I came down here to see if there was anybody – '

'Some people would get all bent out of shape if they knew Kevin and I were living here by ourselves, you know. That's why' – his voice suddenly went to full volume – 'I'M SO MAD! That you had to go poking around here where you DON'T BELONG!'

The sixth step.

'Craig,' she said, her voice almost breaking. 'I saw what you're doing down here. And – '

The seventh step.

I'm close enough to try it, she told herself. Now!

She hurled her body into motion, springing upward as fast as she could.

Except before she could get by him, he held out an arm. It was like running into an iron bar.

Now he was the one moving with lightning speed. The arm hooked around her. He pushed her up against the wall and held her there.

Then he slapped her hard across the face with his free hand. She reached out and clawed his

131

face with her nails. There was a split second of stalemate. He swung again. McKenzie ducked so that Craig's hand hit her mouth and then she sank her teeth into the fleshy heel of his hand, hard.

He screamed and whipped his hand back. Here was her chance to get by him. She lunged toward the doorway.

But he had her by the hair now, yanking her back with all his might.

'HEEEELP!' she screamed.

He seized her neck in both hands, as if to choke the sound right out of her. But her knee came up and caught him in the groin. He doubled over, then fell. He dragged her down the stairs with him.

On her hands and knees she scrambled up the steps past him, scraping her palms on the splintery wood. Almost there, she told herself. But he lunged up and grabbed her foot. She banged back down the steps, hitting her chin on the edge of one step, her forehead on the next.

He had her. He gripped her face in his hands and banged her head against the wood.

She reacted without thinking. 'HEEEEEELP!' she screamed again, even louder, then managed to kick her way to her feet. He got to his feet too, then grabbed her jacket, yanking her to him.

Just then, the basement door opened.

Standing there was Kevin, wide-eyed in terror. He was wearing his coat.

A jumble of thoughts raced through McKenzie's mind. Where had he been? He must have run out when Craig attacked him. It didn't matter. Her heart leaped. Thank goodness he was all right!

'NOOOOOOOOO!' Kevin screamed down at Craig. 'NOOOOOO! STOPPPPPPP!!!!'

'*Get help!*' McKenzie cried.

Shoving McKenzie down to the floor, Craig ran up the stairs. He pushed Kevin out and slammed the door closed.

McKenzie ached all over, but she managed to grab the banister and haul herself into a standing position.

She'd made it halfway up the steps when Craig turned and started coming back toward her. She lunged forward, ramming her right shoulder into his stomach with all her might. With a grunt he staggered back, but he had an arm hooked around her waist.

Then they were tumbling down the stairs, tearing at each other's clothes and hair all the way.

McKenzie's head hit the wall first, and then the floor –

Then she blacked out.

CHAPTER 21

February 14, 7:32 p.m.
. . . tick tick tick tick . . .

A feeling of heat.

The need to cough.

She opened her eyes.

She was lying facedown on the floor of a basement. At first she didn't know where she was. Then she remembered. The Larsen house. The stairs. Falling. The damp cement felt gritty against her cheek. It was hotter than before. Much hotter. Her clothes were soaked with sweat.

She was coughing now. And it wasn't until she stopped coughing that she realized how much her head hurt. Her skull ached as if it were hitting the floor over and over again.

She tried to move. It hurt.

If only she could stay unconscious.

But no, she told herself, there's danger here. She lifted her head, forcing herself to look around.

She was staring right into Craig's face.

He was lying near her, his eyes shut. Was he dead? Or just unconscious?

How long had she been out of it? She checked her watch. The face was smashed. It said seven o'clock. Surely it was later than that. The watch had stopped, probably when she fell down the stairs. Get to your feet, Mack.

I'm trying, she answered herself.

It wasn't easy . . .

Until she smelled something that motivated her.

Smoke.

Was there a fire? Then she remembered.

Craig's cigarette. It must have flown from his mouth during their struggle. In one quick glance around the smoky room McKenzie took in the old newspapers, cardboard boxes, and wooden crates. The cigarette had to be the culprit — because now the piles of old newspapers and boxes were on fire!

McKenzie dragged herself toward the flames, smoke burning her eyes. She got to her feet and tried to stamp out the fire.

Too late. Flames were shooting up all around

her. There was a strange sizzling sound. The hanging sheet had caught. Runners of flame raced across the thin white fabric toward a pile of dirty rags. There was no way she could put out the fire now.

She took Craig by the shoulders and shook him. 'CRAIG!'

No response. Yelling for help, she raced up the crooked stairs. She turned the doorknob. The door wouldn't budge. She threw her whole body against it; still nothing. The door was jammed shut.

'KEVIN! HELP! KEVIN!' she shouted through the door.

She was crying – blinking back the tears – as the acrid smoke stung her eyes. 'I've got to get out! I've got to get out!' she sobbed.

She ran back downstairs. Was there another way out? Before, the answer had seemed to be no. Now she checked again.

There was a small window, high above the Ping-Pong table, that was not covered by the blanket. The fire hadn't reached it . . . yet. Maybe she could get out that way. She shoved the table toward the wall and clambered onto it, coughing. She could just barely reach the window's latch. And now, up close, she realized that the window wasn't big enough for her to climb out of it.

From behind her came a low groan.

Craig had managed to get to his knees. He looked around in horror.

She jumped down off the table. 'We've got to get out of here!'

He staggered to his feet, tried to say something, then simply pointed.

The old sheet had burned to a crisp. McKenzie saw that the fire was about to reach the table piled high with white jars. Jars that were filled with – what?

She looked at Craig's face again – that look of horror.

A series of images flashed through her head, one after another, like wildfire:

The glowing basement door.

Craig selling something from the back of his car.

The lab.

The jars.

She remembered Aidan telling her about the illegal fireworks that kids seemed to get ahold of each year at carnival time. And the terrible accidents. And she realized that Craig wasn't selling drugs at all . . .

Craig was selling homemade firecrackers.

'The gunpowder!' he screamed.

CHAPTER 22

February 14, 7:39 p.m.
. . . TICK TICK TICK . . .

It was the loudest sizzling and crackling McKenzie had ever heard. The green paint on the walls was melting, blistering, popping.

The room was dark with smoke now. Bright yellow flames raged everywhere.

She made her way toward Craig and the stairs. He grabbed her leg, and she reached down to help him.

Craig was pulling himself to his feet. McKenzie became aware of a pounding sound; it took her a second to realize it wasn't just the throbbing in her head. There was someone at the door.

She tried to call for help but choked instead.

The smoke was so thick she could hardly keep her eyes open. They welled up with tears.

Craig was choking too. McKenzie grabbed at his shirt, then tried to pull him toward the stairs. But he was too shaky to walk. McKenzie didn't have to look – she could feel the wall of flame creeping up behind them.

The pounding on the door intensified. It flew open. McKenzie peered through the thickening smoke. *'Aidan!'*

He started down the stairs toward them.

Just then Kevin squirmed past Aidan and came running down the steps. *'No!'* yelled Aidan. 'KEVIN!'

He lunged forward and grabbed Kevin's shirt with his good hand.

But the boy wriggled free and raced down toward his brother and McKenzie.

Suddenly the sizzling grew louder and popping sounds came one after another.

'Hit the floor!' Craig shouted at McKenzie as he lunged forward to grab Kevin.

'Aidan!' screamed McKenzie, ducking behind a pile of crates. Craig reached out toward his brother, but Kevin tripped and fell just as –

KABOOOOOOOOOOOOOOOOOOOOOOOOO-OOOOOM!

The explosion rocked the house, sending objects flying through the air.

CHAPTER 23

Smoke and flames were everywhere.

McKenzie jumped to her feet. Then she saw Kevin, soaked with blood, lying on the floor near Craig.

At the same moment she saw someone stumbling down the stairs. She glimpsed the face through the smoke – Aidan!

The fire roared around them. Aidan made his way down the stairs through the rubble to pick up Kevin.

Craig groaned, and McKenzie dragged him to his feet.

'Follow me!' Aidan screamed at them as he began the climb back up the stairs with Kevin in his arms. Covering their faces, McKenzie and Craig started toward the stairway.

They picked their way through the rubble, one step at a time. McKenzie couldn't help thinking that just minutes ago Craig had done his best to make sure she would never get out of his basement alive. And now he was leaning on her for support! But she pushed these thoughts from her mind. The important thing right now was to get out before there was another explosion.

They'd made it to the top! Just outside the basement McKenzie fell to the floor, sucking in mouthfuls of air. Craig collapsed beside her. Aidan rushed on ahead, Kevin in his arms; he kicked the front door open ahead of him. He turned back. 'C'mon!'

McKenzie pulled on Craig's arm, trying to follow. 'C'mon,' she tried to say, but no sounds came out. Spasms of coughing took hold of her.

Moments later Aidan was back, pawing at her with his broken hand. He couldn't pull her up with the cast. 'Go!' she managed. She was on her feet now, lifting up Craig.

Finally they were outside, gulping in clear air, staggering with relief. It was so dark out. Or was it just her blurred vision? She and Craig were both coughing horribly, rubbing their eyes. She was groggy. Craig was bent over double. Aidan was carrying Kevin toward

Craig's run-down yellow car. He draped the boy across the backseat. His white shirt was now splattered with Kevin's blood.

Craig tried to get into the driver's seat, but Aidan pushed him in farther, shouting, 'I'll drive!'

There was no room left in the small car. 'You stay. I'll drive,' McKenzie insisted as another fit of coughing overtook her.

Aidan's good hand clasped her; its cuff was drenched with Kevin's blood. 'You can't, Mack. You're in no condition. Forget it. Let Craig wait. You're coming with me to the hospital.'

In the passenger seat Craig was slumped over, passed out cold. 'We can't just throw him out in the snow,' she said. 'I could follow in my mother's car, but – then you'd be driving. What time is it?'

'I forgot my watch. I ran so fast when Kevin called, I didn't put it on. I hitched a ride. It's early yet, I think. Hey, look, I'm wearing a white shirt, it's not snowing, and I'll be at the hospital in fifteen minutes. I gotta go, Mack. The kid is bleeding to death in there!'

'All right,' she said. What choice did they have? 'Go now. You have to get there before seven fifty. At the latest! Go!'

'Will you be okay?' Aidan asked.

McKenzie nodded – she didn't trust her voice.

Aidan jumped in the car and backed up past her in a wild rush; he missed the driveway and bumped wildly over the curb.

In the distance she heard the wail of fire sirens approaching. A crowd was beginning to form outside the house. Normally she would have stayed to talk to the police and fire department. But there was nothing normal about this situation. She had to follow Aidan, make sure he was safe.

She hopped into the seat of her mother's car and started it. Then she saw the dashboard clock. Seven fifty-two. It was later than either of them had thought. Too late. Aidan wouldn't make it to the hospital in time!

She screeched out after the rapidly disappearing yellow car. All at once the pieces had come together in her head.

Aidan was driving, with one hand just like in the vision. She'd seen that the cuff of his shirt was red. But now she realized it wasn't a red shirt. It was a white shirt soaked with blood! She glanced up. The sky was purple with snow clouds.

The images came back to her . . .

Aidan driving, driving with only his left

hand, the red cuff of the shirt, the Band-Aid on his cheek . . .

A fat snowflake landed on her windshield.

Her vision! It was all coming true!

CHAPTER 24

February 14, 7:56 p.m.
TICK TICK TICK . . .

The ticking had started again, deep within her brain, louder than ever before.

She stepped on the gas. She was honking wildly. 'Aidan – stop!'

But he didn't hear, didn't stop. Nothing could make him stop now.

She was driving as fast as she could down the icy, dark street. She had to catch up with him!

She tried to pass him to the left on a narrow street; a truck was coming toward her, and she had to pull quickly back.

She rolled down her window, letting in the snow and cold. She leaned her head out as she drove. 'AIDAN!' The yellow Lion pulled away. Her voice was lost in the wind.

On her radio the deejay crooned, 'Love songs! We've got nothing but love songs, all day long. Happy Valentine's Day, rock-'n'-roll fans.'

TICK TICK TICK . . .

Aidan ran a red light. She followed him. A large van skidded to a halt in the middle of the slick intersection, the driver waving his arms at her in fury.

But wait! Think, Mack! The ticking in her nightmare. She had assumed it was a bomb.

Now she knew. Craig was selling ashcans from the trunk of his car at the mall. So then his trunk must still be filled with ashcans – with gunpowder!

TICK TICK TICK . . .

The ticking in her head was violently loud now. What was it trying to tell her?

Don't be stupid again, McKenzie screamed at herself. Think!

But the noise in her head, the tears in her eyes from the smoke, the coughs that racked her – all made it so hard to think clearly. Let alone drive faster than she had ever driven before . . .

TICK TICK TICK . . .

What if the ticking sound that had been haunting her for days wasn't the sound of a bomb at all? What if it was just the sound of time passing, counting down the seconds to that crucial moment ... the moment in her vision when the clock hand jabbed forward?

Two minutes to eight.

Which was –

She cut a glance at the clock on the dashboard – *only seconds from now!*

Even as she thought that, she saw Aidan swerve onto Montague.

She turned hard after him.

TICK TICK TICK!

And saw – too late – that Aidan had pulled up short, just around the corner, right in front of the hospital.

TICK TICK TICK!

Oh no! she thought. She was going to rear end Craig's car!

So she herself would be the one to cause the explosion!

TICK TICK TICK!

McKenzie jammed on the brakes.

She skidded across the ice.

She tried to swerve out of the way.

But it was no use.

It all happened so fast.

TICK TICK TICK!

The back of Craig's car rushed toward her.

CHAPTER 25

BAM!

She smashed into the back of Craig's car at almost full speed. Despite her seat belt, her head slammed forward against the wheel.

TICK TICK TICK!

She forced herself to keep moving. She staggered out of the car.

TICK TICK TICK – the ticking in her head was screamingly loud now.

She reached the yellow car. Aidan was slumped forward over the steering wheel. She yanked open the door and pulled his head back.

Blood streamed from his nose and mouth. His eyes were closed.

'AIDAN!'

She tried to pull him from the car. He came to and held on to her.

'AIDAN!'

He was beginning to get his feet back under him.

'OUT OF THE CAR!' She was screaming, out of control, the sound ripping out of her. 'IT'S GOING TO EXPLODE!'

TICK   TICK   TICK!

Smoke began pouring from the back of the yellow Lion.

She raced to the other side of the car. Aidan followed her. 'BACK!' she screamed. But Aidan helped pull out Craig.

'RUN!' McKenzie threw everything into the yell, as if she could propel Aidan and Craig away from the car with her voice alone.

TICK   TICK   TICK!

She could hear the loud popping of fireworks in the trunk. She bent over the backseat, one arm under Kevin's head, the other under his knees. He moaned softly as she pulled him out of the car.

'RUN!' she yelled again.

They were all moving now. Craig had come to and leaned heavily on Aidan. Kevin was in her arms as they slipped across the icy parking lot outside the big white hospital –

T   I   C   K

Then the ticking in her ticked one last time. And stopped. That fraction of a second's pause.

'HIT THE GROUND!' she cried.

She fell first, aiming at a snowbank. She cradled Kevin in her arms, tried to keep her body from landing on top of his.

She was aware of Aidan and Craig falling to the ground nearby.

As they fell the flames reached the fuel tank. And the yellow car exploded.

CHAPTER 26

'Happy Valentine's Day'

The noise was deafening.

McKenzie turned her head back toward the car and saw the luminous white fireball mushrooming upward. Caught in the billowing flames were chunks of the car – a door, a trunk lid – all flying up and out.

Glass rained down, spitting against the hard black pavement like hail.

A twisted hunk of metal sizzled into the snow only three feet from McKenzie's head.

And then, at last, everything was quiet except for the crackling of the orange flames.

Aidan burst through the white swinging doors into the hospital waiting room and headed toward the blue vinyl sofa where McKenzie sat. He stopped short and grinned.

'Let's see,' McKenzie said.

He obligingly held back the bangs of his unruly sandy hair. A large white bandage covered the cut. 'Only three stitches,' he said. He seemed genuinely pleased.

A generous helping of bruises and cuts were scattered over McKenzie's arms and face. But she had escaped with less serious injuries than he had. No stitches.

'Craig got off with barely a scratch. But he has a concussion from his fall down the stairs. Where's Kevin?' Aidan asked.

She got up and led the way to Kevin's room.

The boy smiled when he saw Aidan.

'Hey,' Aidan said.

'Hi.'

'Kevin's lucky,' McKenzie explained, brushing his brown hair with her hand. 'It could have been a lot worse. Five stitches for the cut on his forehead, and three for his cheek. And some assorted bruises.'

'They want me to stay overnight,' Kevin told them. He didn't look too happy about the idea.

'They want to play it safe,' McKenzie said. 'But we're going to stay here with him, right?'

Aidan was looking past her.

A large woman with blond hair and heavy makeup stood by the open door. She was staring at Kevin, clutching her purse, with a look of terrible fear and guilt.

'Mrs. Larsen!' Aidan said.

Kevin didn't move.

'Kevin,' she said, moving slowly across the room. 'Oh, baby, are you okay?'

He didn't answer. 'He's okay,' McKenzie said. 'So is Craig.'

Mrs. Larsen was holding Kevin's arm, kissing his hand, pressing it against her face, tears already flowing down her cheeks. 'Kevin,' she said, 'I'm so sorry. Oh, my baby. Are you okay? Does it hurt?'

He shrugged off her hands. 'Where have you been?' he asked angrily.

'Oh, baby,' she cried. 'I . . . I . . . I had to get away, baby, just to try to get my head together because . . . I was so upset about Daddy leaving, but . . .'

She stopped, crying harder; a tear escaped from Kevin's left eye, and as it rolled slowly down his cheek his lip began to tremble.

'You've got to believe me, I thought Craig could handle it. I mean, he's always had a temper, like his father. But I never thought that anything like this would happen!'

She looked at Kevin, then away.

'I'm so sorry, baby. Please forgive me. I will

153

never leave you again. I swear it. And I'll make sure that Craig . . . gets help.'

The blare of a walkie-talkie pulled McKenzie's attention away from Kevin and his mom. A policeman entered. 'Mrs. Larsen?' he asked. 'Officer Maris. May I talk to you?'

They stood to one side, but McKenzie could hear enough snatches of their conversation to gather what was said. Craig was going to go to a juvenile detention center. Mrs. Larsen began to cry quietly. 'Craig was always a problem,' she sobbed. 'I should have paid more attention to him.'

When the policeman left, Mrs. Larsen told McKenzie and Aidan, 'You can go. I'm going to stay with him tonight.'

Tears had begun to pour down Kevin's cheeks. He held his arms outstretched. It was Aidan he hugged.

'I'm going to see you in class on Saturday, okay, pal?' Aidan told him.

Kevin nodded. McKenzie gave him a kiss.

Mrs. Larsen watched with her head bowed. 'I don't think I can ever repay you,' she told Aidan. 'In fact, I know I can't.'

He patted her shoulder. And then they left.

'It was all my fault, Mr. Gold,' Aidan said from the backseat of the Golds' other car. McKenzie was sitting right beside him, cuddling against him for warmth. He squeezed her tight with his good hand.

'We'll talk about that later,' Mr. Gold said grimly. His eyes were focused on the icy road.

'When we're safe at home,' added Mrs. Gold.

'We're safe now,' Aidan whispered to McKenzie.

'Why?' McKenzie whispered back.

Aidan looked out the window. They were crossing Tomzack Bridge. 'Don't you see? We made it. I escaped my fate,' he said dramatically.

She looked at his glittering eyes. They seemed to warm her up. It was true. She *could* finally relax. This time, the safety was real. This time, they were free. But were they?

As if he saw the doubt flicker in her eyes, he clutched her hand. 'Hey. Nothing can get me now.'

Suddenly Shelby hit a patch of ice and began to skid.

The car headed right off the bridge.

At the last second, Shelby managed to right the car.

They stayed parked there for a moment, nobody saying a word.

Except for the deejay on the radio. 'Okay, all

you lovers out there,' he said, 'how about one last Valentine's Day smooch for Big Al?'

By then Aidan and McKenzie were laughing crazily.

They waited until they were safe at home before they followed Big Al's suggestion.